A HISTORY OF MEDICINE

IN

SOUTH CAROLINA
1900 - 1970

BY

JOSEPH IOOR WARING, M.D.
The Medical University of South Carolina
CHARLESTON, S. C.

Published by the South Carolina Medical Association

Manufactured in the United States of America by
The R. L. Bryan Co., Columbia, South Carolina, 1971

To my wife, Ferdinanda Legaré Waring

FOREWORD

The two volumes which preceded this one attempted to bring the story of medicine in South Carolina up to the year 1900. The present volume offers a continuation of this account into the twentieth century, as nearly up to date as possible. It is the story of the medical profession in South Carolina and its activities. It makes no pretense of recording those tremendous advances in medical art and science which have characterized this period. It seeks to give a background of relatively recent events which have led up to the current activities of organized medicine in the state and to record some of the lives of the people who are woven into the fabric of the story.

The sources of the information included in this volume have been numerous. Much help has been obtained from many individuals and organizations. Some details may be subject to revision but the author has tried to select what seemed to be the most reliable accounts. He has had the continued cheerful and efficient help of the same people who aided so much in the earlier publications, *viz.* Miss Desmond Koster and Miss Elizabeth Williams of the Health Affairs Library of the Medical University of South Carolina, Miss Virginia Rugheimer, Mrs. Beulah Sheetz, and Mrs. Pringle Haigh of the Charleston Library Society, Mr. E. L. Inabinett and Mrs. Clara Mae Jacobs of the South Caroliniana Library, and Mrs. Granville T. Prior of the South Carolina Historical Society.

This book does not pretend to be a well organized historical narrative, but concentrates rather on recording events and persons of the period. It assumes somewhat the nature of a handbook, which may be useful in recognizing the origins and progress of current activities of our medical organizations.

Research and preparation of material for this book has been made possible through the generous aid of Public Health Service Grants 1 R01 LM 00528-01 and 02 from the Department of Health, Education, and Welfare.

For able and valuable assistance in preparation of the manuscript the author is indebted to Mrs. Anne Donato. Publication has been supported generously by the South Carolina Medical Association.

JOSEPH I. WARING, M.D.

TABLE OF CONTENTS

[vii]

CHAPTER 1

THE DOCTOR OF 1900 IN SOUTH CAROLINA

In 1900, thirty-five years after the end of the Civil War, South Carolina was still in a state of political and economic turmoil. Strong feeling between the upper and the lower classes was rife. In general, the "aristocracy" of the time was based chiefly on the possession of ample worldly goods; the truly aristocratic flavor of certain elements surviving in some parts of the state, especially in the Charleston area, was resented by those who were regarded by these elements as having less pride in birth and background. Senator Ben Tillman had been the champion of the masses, and the farmers' movement had been productive of a modest betterment of their condition. Politics were violently active. Threats of bloodshed and actual lynchings were not infrequent. The Negro had little voice in any public activities, was completely segregated, and seldom voted.

South Carolina was still basically a rural state in considerable economic distress. Crops of the time were good, but most farms were mortgaged and the price of cotton was extremely low. The ancient culture of rice was declining very rapidly and corn and tobacco were developing as important crops. Textile mills in the upper part of the state were increasing in number and, at the same time, in production of health problems for their workers. Charleston, the chief port, had a reasonably active commerce, but discriminatory freight rates retarded its development. With eggs at 14¢ a dozen and good shoes at $2.50 a pair, living should have been easy, but there was very little money available with which to purchase the necessary commodities.

Twenty per cent of the adults of the state were illiterate and another twenty per cent nearly so. Politics absorbed much of the energy and talent that might have been directed to better purposes. The horse and buggy still provided transportation for the doctor and others; the automobile was just turning the corner. The scandal of the state whiskey dispensaries was still in the air.

The picture of disease had changed from that of the 19th century. Yellow fever and cholera had apparently had their last flings. Smallpox was still relatively common and malaria and typhoid fever continued to be major causes of disease and death. Infant

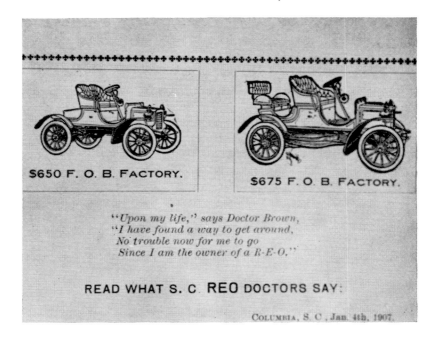

$650 F. O. B. FACTORY.

$675 F. O. B. FACTORY.

*"Upon my life," says Doctor Brown,
"I have found a way to get around,
No trouble now for me to go
Since I am the owner of a R-E-O."*

READ WHAT S. C. REO DOCTORS SAY:

COLUMBIA, S. C., Jan. 4th, 1907.

and maternal mortality rates were high. Proper vital statistics were lacking. There was no organized effort to promote health in schools, no state clinics for children or mothers, no regulation of the milk supply, and no canned foods for infants to simplify the mother's life. The federal grants for health purposes so common today were not even envisioned. Tuberculosis was abundant and on the rise, and there were no provisions for hospital care of its victims.

South Carolina had just over 1100 physicians in 1900. Charleston, a city of nearly 56,000 people, had a fairly large and active profession. Columbia had some 21,000 inhabitants, Greenville and Spartanburg less than 12,000 each, and Florence showed fewer than 5,000. The medical school of the state had been long established since 1824 and had gone through various vicissitudes. In 1900 it was in the position of being a proprietary school with a dedicated type of faculty fortunately concerned with teaching rather than with financial gain.

Eighty per cent of South Carolinians lived outside of the cities. The large Negro population, which made up a considerable majority of the people of the state, had relatively little medical care available and was afflicted with many superstitions and prejudices which made efforts for improving its health conditions difficult.

Charleston had provided hospitals of various kinds since its earlier days. The State Insane Asylum had been in operation in Columbia since 1828. Roper Hospital in Charleston was completed in 1852. The Columbia Hospital of 25 beds had been opened in 1893. The St. Francis Xavier Infirmary, a Catholic institution, began its operations in Charleston in 1882. Small hospitals, privately promoted, had appeared in a number of the towns of the state, e.g., Florence, Greenville, Columbia, Aiken, Sumter, and Spartanburg. The new century was to see a rapid increase in the number and quality of hospital institutions.

The number of physicians in the state had not increased greatly in the preceding years of limited economic opportunity. Most of them were products of their own state medical school. The rest had attended medical schools in other parts of the country, without any particular favoritism. They were all licensed by the state, but licensing requirements were not stringent. They were still traveling poor roads with primitive transportation. They were men of varying ability and many of them did little to keep abreast of the advances of medicine. For financial reasons, not many attended medical conventions or pursued post-graduate instruction. Those who were members of the South Carolina Medical Association had the opportunity of hearing scientific presentations at the annual meeting of that body, but scientific activities in county medical societies, and indeed activities of any kind in county medical societies, were often minimal. The physician had to read to keep abreast. Not yet was he flooded with the spate of medical literature that washes over the doctor's desk of today.

The South Carolina Medical Association, founded in 1848, had experienced its ups and downs, even to the point of complete inactivity during the Civil War. Recovery in organized medical activities after that tragedy was slow and unsatisfactory. In the period just before 1900 most of the county and district medical societies were stagnant. Attendance at the meetings of the state organization was at a rather low level, nor was membership coveted particularly by the larger element of practitioners. The annual meeting of 1900 included only 146 physicians. This apathetic attitude among the physicians was deplored periodically by the Association, although by 1909 it had achieved a membership of 727. There was no medical journal published in the state in the 20th century until 1905. About this time, under the impetus of the American Medical Association, reorganization and reactivation for many of the county medical societies took place and a new era began in organized medicine in South Carolina.

In the light of present day potentials, the physician of 1900 was considerably handicapped by his deficiencies in what is now common knowledge of the medical art and of the many elaborate techniques generally employed. In his day, two great instruments of medical practice, the telephone and the automobile, were just coming into general use; outside of a few large centers, the practitioner was still the horse and buggy doctor.

The great textbook of the period was Osler's *Practice of Medicine* and the pages of the edition of 1909 (there were earlier and later editions) give a good picture of what little the practitioner of the day might accomplish.[1] Although actual cure of disease was a rarity, the doctor of 1909 excelled in making keen clinical observations, most of which have stood the test of time. Research in its present sense was in its infancy and the discoveries of years just passed had not been so firmly established that they made up a very practical part of the average doctor's armamentarium.

The theories of Freud had been enunciated only a few years before. A number of germs had been discovered, and in the years before 1900 a few more etiological factors had been clarified in the identification of the trypanosome organisms and those of dysentery. The x-ray had been discovered only five years before and was not used extensively in clinical medicine. Radium had been put into use only two years before 1900. In 1899 the mosquito transmission of yellow fever was established. Although the great Johns Hopkins Medical School was founded in 1889, the medical schools of the country were in general still of the type of the proprietary schools of the late 1800's.

The doctor of 1900 dealt with most of the diseases of today, though the emphasis was on certain conditions now less prevalent. Typhoid fever was a great problem, with a mortality rate of 33.8 per 100,000. Typhoid vaccine was first used in 1904, but treatment of the disease was still purely supportive. Specific antibiotic treatment was not to be developed until some 50 years later. Osler gave a clinical description of the disease which has not been surpassed. Pneumonia, "the friend of the aged", was prevalent then as now. The physician could only prescribe the best of intensive nursing care and sit by waiting hopefully for the crisis which would put a dramatic end to the course of lobar pneumonia. Although there was an unexplained decrease in the mortality of pneumonia after 1900, there was still no specific treatment.

The cause of syphilis was found in 1905, and the diagnostic laboratory tests followed almost immediately. The discovery of salvarsan as a near-specific treatment came in 1909. The clinical picture of syphilis in its many manifestations was well recognized; with the advent of new treatments there were considerable changes in its character, but the doctor of 1900 could not foresee this. The role of the streptococcus in rheumatic fever was only suspected, and no connection was recognized between that disease and the throat infections which preceded the manifestations of the attack. Therapy in this disorder was chiefly with salicylates, pre-aspirin compounds which were reasonably palliative. The use of specific antibiotic treatment was far in the future.

The diseases due to vitamin deficiency were well known in their clinical manifestations, but the causative bases were unsuspected. James Lind had long ago eliminated scurvy from the British naval vessels by the use of lemon juice and many years before 1900 pellagra had been cured by empiric treatment with proper diet. The concept of avitaminosis was in the distance; beri-beri, for instance, was classified by Osler in 1909 as due to some form of obscure poisoning. Of arthritis deformans (rheumatoid arthritis) almost as much was known then as is now, when effective specific treatment still awaits development. There were none of the modern drugs which give adequate palliation in this disorder. Diabetes was treated entirely by diet; the method of determination of blood-sugar was not discovered until 1909. For diseases of the liver and kidney there was little to be done. Even as late as 1909 Osler occasionally used bleeding in quantities of 15 to 20 ounces in certain conditions. The serious anemias were still obscure. The causes of Hodgkin's Disease, diseases of the suprarenals, and exophthalmic goiter were unknown. For the last named condition some patients were treated effectively with radiation and surgery, somewhat in the modern manner. Myxoedema was baffling; angina pectoris was treated then as now; tabes and paresis, later recognized as syphilitic, were not to have the benefit of the specific treatment with salvarsan until some years after its discovery.

Our modern doctor rejoices in a variety of drugs and methods of cure which were entirely lacking in 1900. One might wonder whether this modern physician has the same sharp powers of observation which supported his predecessors. It has been stated that "at the level of clinical and pathological description of the natural history of disease nothing substantial has been added since Osler's resume of 1909".[2]

The lack of definitively curative drugs had led earlier to the doctrine of therapeutic nihilism, a principle derived largely from the Paris school of medicine. Respect for the profession was somewhat on the rise. Its status had improved during the last quarter of the 19th century from a time when it had fallen to a rather low ebb. The physician was occupied in attending a great number of patients, perhaps seeing 40 to 60 in a day (not unusual today!), with much relatively slow travel. In 1900 there was said to be an excessive supply of physicians.

The surgeon had little defense against the staphylococci and streptococci with their constant threat of dangerous infection. Burns were treated with zinc oxide, starch, and perhaps bichloride of mercury. Dry sterile linens were beginning to replace wet drapes. Septicemia was still the surgeon's nemesis, but new techniques of anesthesia were extending his field, while the skills derived from development of specialism were opening up wide ranges for exploitation. The first successful appendectomy had already been done in 1887,[3] and surgical possibilities were expanding. Psychiatry was moving from the somatic to the psychological approach and was beginning its travels toward becoming a "social science".

REFERENCES

1. A. McG. Harvey and Victor A. McKusick, *Osler's Textbook Revisited* (New York: Appleton Century-Crofts 1968).

2. *Ibid*, p. 361.

3. J. Collins Warren and A. Pearce Gould, *International Textbook on Surgery* (Philadelphia: W. B. Saunders and Co. 1900), Vol. 1 *passim*.

CHAPTER 2

THE SOUTH CAROLINA MEDICAL ASSOCIATION
AFTER 1900

In the spring of 1900 the South Carolina Medical Association, founded in 1848, held what is was pleased to call its semi-centennial meeting. There were 146 of its 311 members present, an indication that the activity of the Association was still rather small. In order to stimulate interest Dr. W. Peyre Porcher gave a sketch of the life of the organization and, along with Dr. J. L. Dawson, strongly urged the publication of a journal to fill the need for a medical organ in the state. Notice was taken of the unfriendly attitude of the legislature toward health measures; that body had even granted the requests of the medical students in Charleston, supported by part of the faculty, that they be exempt from the requirements of the Board of Medical Examiners. A committee of the Association was appointed to go before the medically apathetic lawmakers to oppose such improper efforts, and was successful in having the undesirable act repealed.

The significant changes which were taking place in national and local medical affairs were evident in the reorganization of the American Medical Association in 1901. New emphasis was placed on the importance of the functions of county medical societies, which were now to become the units which determined the eligibility of applicants for both the state and national associations. The House of Delegates was revamped, with a limited membership proportionate to the number of members of the state associations, thereby eliminating the previously overbalanced voting strength of local attendants at annual "general meetings".

In the years just subsequent to 1900 a number of changes were made in the South Carolina association's procedure. By 1902 the practice of having guest speakers at the annual meeting had been adopted. There was already talk of acquiring a permanent home. The meeting of this year was enlivened and protracted by the trial ("with hisses") of a member accused and convicted of numerous malpractices. Adoption of a new constitution and bylaws by the Association followed approval by the American Medical Association, with its similar provisions and a new code of ethics. With these new rules, delegates were elected to the state House of Delegates by the county societies, one for each 20 members or fraction thereof. The House of Delegates included councillors, the president, and the secretary. At the time three vice-presidents held office. Members qualified as honorary fellows after 30 years membership.

Efforts to increase membership were having considerable success. The meeting of 1903 could show delegates from 22 counties, representing a membership which included however only one-third of the total potential. The House of Delegates busied itself with emphasis on the need for an adequate law to govern medical practice and offered much complaint of the current malpractices of cultists and the abuse of patent medicines. Lack of proper vital statistics also was among its concerns.

A systematic effort for the reorganization of county societies was carried out at this time. After much activity on the part of Dr. J. N. McCormack of Kentucky, official organizer employed by the American Medical Association for the purpose, a membership of 385 (including representatives from 40 counties) could be reported in 1905. Dr. T. G. Simons could note an improved attitude of the legislature toward the Board of Health, still suffering from legislative penury, and reported the passage of laws for compulsory smallpox vaccination. A most important advance was in the resolution to publish a state medical journal and the selection of Drs. Robert Wilson, T. P. Whaley, and C. P. Aimar as an editorial board.

The appearance of the *Journal* in June 1905 under the editorship of Dr. Robert Wilson produced a rapid increase in interest in state medical affairs and the publication proved to be a powerful cohesive factor in stimulating organization and individual concern. Beside the *Journal,* the Association also published a *Councillor's Bulletin* which appeared bi-monthly for a short time. By this time the South Carolina Medical Association was beginning to assume a solid and important position in the affairs of the state and in national medical activities.

In 1906 official relations between doctors and legislators must have been reasonably cordial, for the annual meeting of the Association was held in the House of Representatives. There were now 587 members on the rolls, and all counties except Beaufort, Berkeley, Chesterfield, and Lancaster were affiliated. Dr. Walter Cheyne was secretary. The county societies were greatly concerned about the difference in fees paid by various insurance companies for examinations. Greenwood County, irked by the activities of those

The Journal OF THE South Carolina Medical Association

PUBLISHED EVERY MONTH UNDER THE DIRECTION OF THE
COMMITTEE ON PUBLICATION.

OFFICE OF PUBLICATION, 4 VANDERHORST STREET CHARLESTON. S. C.

Entered as second-class matter June 21st, 1905, at the post-office at Charleston, S. C.,
under the act of Congress of March 3, 1879.

Vol. I	Charleston, S. C. June 21, 1905	No. 1

CONTENTS

preachers who recommended nostrums, cut these trespassers from the "free list".

In 1906 an amendment was passed making the chairman of the Executive Committee of the State Board of Health and the chairman of the State Board of Medical Examiners *ex officio* members of the House of Delegates. An official seal was designed by Drs. Robert Wilson and T. P. Whaley and adopted by the Association. The design was described as "A mountain rising above a sea, and around the former is coiled a serpent, the emblem of Esculapius, holding a lighted torch in his mouth—around the margins are inscribed the words graven over the three gateways erected by Dr. Caius at Cambridge—Virtue, Honor, Wisdom, Humility".

In this year Dr. Robert Wilson resigned as editor of *The Journal* and Dr. J. W. Jervey was appointed in his place. In the next year

interest in insurance fees was still so vital that the Greenville and Spartanburg societies expelled certain members who were accepting $3.00 instead of the usual $5.00 fee for examinations. The House of Delegates, whose activities were still viewed with suspicion by some members, resolved to pay expenses of the delegate to the American Medical Association. It also passed a resolution banning "commissions" on fees—*i. e.*, fee-splitting.

The Anderson meeting of 1908 was marked by interest in the new Medical Practice Act providing for changes in the method of appointment of the medical examiners, for the revocation of medical licenses for cause, for the requirement of four years of medical schooling for applicants, for the abolition of the clause exempting from examination those physicians who had practiced for five years, and for licensing of osteopaths and homeopaths. Great credit was given to Dr. LeGrand Guerry, the president, for his energetic efforts to secure passage of the bill. At this meeting a resolution was adopted whereby the secretary became *ex officio* a delegate to the American Medical Association. Increasing concern over tuberculosis was evident over the state, and plans were laid for organization of anti-tuberculosis associations in all the counties. Members of the Association were urged to run for legislative offices in order to increase the power of the profession in determining medical and public health legislation.

An important progressive step was accomplished by the legislative creation of the position of state health officer, whose executive responsibility it would be to carry out the instructions of the State Board of Health—*i. e.*, the whole membership of the Association acting through its elected Executive Committee. The Board of Health announced the imminent opening of a laboratory which would furnish, among other things, material for antirabic inoculation.

In 1909 a committee with Dr. C. W. Kollock as chairman was formed to raise funds for a memorial to Dr. J. Marion Sims, and began a creeping progress to a final conclusion many years later. Being in the mood for commendation, the Association likewise adopted a resolution that a tablet be placed in the hall of the Medical Society of South Carolina in honor of Dr. Francis Peyre Porcher, author of *Resources of the Southern Fields and Forests* and prominent participant in the earlier activities of the Association, but there is no concrete indication that this resolution was carried out. The Medical Examiners recommended that candidates for licenses must have high school diplomas, a refinement which was not adopted as a requirement for admission to the Medical College until the following year.

The meeting in 1910 was in the town of Laurens. Dr. J. C. Sosnowski succeeded Dr. F. H. McLeod as editor of the *Journal,* and Dr. Walter Cheyne, secretary for many sessions, was succeeded by Dr. Edgar A. Hines, who was to hold this office for a very long term of valuable and active years. An Anti-Tuberculosis Committee was formed.

The meeting of 1911 in Charleston was marred by the death of Dr. Manning Simons, and the many planned entertainments were omitted. Interest centered on an act proposed in the legislature whereby the nomination of the members of the Board of Medical Examiners would be the political privilege of the senators from the several districts. A proposal that the examiners themselves be examined by the College faculty failed to achieve serious recognition.

In 1912 the offices of secretary and treasurer were combined, and Dr. Hines took over the editorial chair of the *Journal* from Dr. Sosnowski. The Society of Medical Secretaries (*i. e.*, county secretaries) held its fourth meeting.

Rock Hill entertained the Association in 1913, the year in which the Medical College became a state institution. Membership was then about 700. Drs. William Weston and Edgar Hines worked on projects for public education, and offered to the legislature free services of physicians if the proposed bill for school inspection were passed.

In 1914 the *Journal* was active and flourishing. Workers from the American Medical Association were busy organizing county societies. The Sims Committee was in the doldrums and suggested that the proposed memorial be in the form of a library or a hospital or an endowed chair at the Medical College. A bill for recording of vital statistics was passed. The citizens of Charleston donated a $75,000 building to the Medical School, then rated in Class B, but in two years to become a Class A medical institution.

Association business was quiet in 1915. It was noted that only one newspaper in the state, the Greenwood *Index*, refused quack medical advertisements, and due commendation of this attitude was recorded.

War was coming close in 1916, and the Association became active in "medical preparedness", organizing a committee with Dr. R. S. Cathcart as chairman and preparing for the inevitable.

The rapid growth of hospitals over the state might well have left something to be desired in their inexperienced managements, and in 1916 Dr. Robert Wilson made the unchallenged statement that our hospitals in general were poorly managed, had poor records, few laboratory facilities, and no attraction for interns or research workers; no doubt this comment was the reason for the appointment by the Association of a standing Committee on Hospitals in 1917.

The advent of that year saw hastened preparation for war and the absorption of many members of the profession by the armed services. Those who remained at home agreed to care for the patients of the physicians in service and to turn over to their absent colleagues one third of the fees collected, but this plan proved neither popular nor workable.

In 1918 the state was full of troops. Of the 738 members of the Association, 225 were in the services and those left at home were wrestling with the pandemic influenza. Whether or not to use whiskey in the disease was the burning question of the time. The *Journal* shrank, consisting largely of abstracts. In the midst of the activities of war an Infant Mortality Committee was organized and began at once to make efforts to save more babies for more wars. This increased concern for the health of children was a subject which had already occupied interested people in Columbia and Charleston.

The doctors were coming back in 1918, most of them, but influenza had exacted its permanent quota. They were faced with a difficult period of readjustment and redistribution and had to offer active competition to the irregular practitioners who were flourishing in the state. Efforts at control of these undesirable gentry and actual prosecution were seldom successful.

With the backing and encouragement of the Association, South Carolina passed a school medical inspection bill, inaugurated hotel inspection, and made physical examination of school teachers mandatory. The growing interest in health in children was indicated by the development of a Bureau of Child Hygiene in the State Board of Health. A new Medical Practice Act provided eight members for the Board of Medical Examiners with terms of four years. Members were to be nominated by the Association and appointed by the governor and they were given the power of revocation of licenses for cause. Requirements for examination were now set at four years experience at medical school and possession of a medical degree.

In 1921 the State Hospital Association was formed by the House of Delegates, and the South Carolina Public Health Association was organized. The Southern Pediatric Seminar at Saluda, N. C., largely an effort of South Carolinians, began operation and the South Carolina Pediatric Society met for the first time. There were two distinct rumblings to be heard at the annual meeting of the Association, one a yearning for more available postgraduate instruction, and the other a grumbling from certain quarters about the condition of the *Journal*.

In 1922 it was noted that the legislators were again attempting to assume the right of appointment of the members of the Executive Committee of the State Board of Health and threatening to put the tuberculosis sanatorium under the Board of Welfare, but better politics prevailed and the bills were rejected, as was the bill for licensing chiropractors. The Woman's Auxiliary was formed. The *Journal* took on new life under fire, and a committee to revise the constitution began to function.

Hospitals were increasing greatly in number. It was noted in the *Journal* that before the recent development of hospitals Charleston had maintained a monopoly of hospitals and specialists, and that the Charlestonian specialists would often travel far over the state in order to perform necessary surgical operations.

In 1923 the Committee on Scientific Work was established. The Association had reached a peak with a membership of 916. Activity of some county societies was sometimes rather slight and attendance was often made up of five or six members. By this time seven full time health departments had been established in the state and public health work was developing rapidly. The quacks were still active; the popular apparatus of the day was the Abrams box, which reputedly performed wonders. Even a few of the legitimate members of the Association took after this will-o'-the-wisp.

The expressed desire of the membership of the Association for postgraduate instruction within easy range was fulfilled in part by the establishment of courses of two weeks duration at the Medical College in 1927.

After twenty years of effort, in 1929 the Sims Memorial achieved substance in the form of a monument on the State House grounds. The *Journal* was still under discussion. In the years of depression the cost of medical care was often under lengthy consideration.

In 1930 agitation concerning economic affairs continued. The president warned against the encroachment of public health measures, clinics, and free vaccines on the income of the practitioner. Times were hard. The Charleston society protested against free clinics as deleterious to its members' practices. Workmen's compensation laws were before the legislature. During the next few years these were the chief concerns of the Association.

A move to merge some of the smaller county societies was accomplished. In 1931 the Columbia Society became the largest in South Carolina. In 1933 a Committee on Public Instruction undertook to publish in the lay press authoritative articles on medical subjects for the benefit of the citizens of the state. The *Journal* was still unpopular with some of the members. In 1932 Dr. Robert Wilson resigned from the Executive Committee of the State Board of Health after 35 years as a member and 25 years as chairman. In recognition of his exceedingly valuable services he was presented by the Association with a testimonial set of silver.

In 1934 postgraduate obstetrical courses were sponsored by the Association and were given about the state. A Cancer Committee was formed. The Association was now concerned with the proposals of the Federal Emergency Relief Administration, especially in regard to the decrease in medical fees. Its membership had decreased to 636, perhaps an indication of the still prevalent hard times. The presidential address included a recommendation for health insurance by medical societies, but no action was taken on the suggestion. The Medical College inaugurated an annual Founders Day Post-Graduate program. The Piedmont Postgraduate Assembly was organized at Anderson in 1936. The Columbia Medical Society, still the largest county society, started in 1937 a program of invited speakers and the publication of a monthly bulletin, *The Recorder*.

In 1937 the headquarters of the Association were established at Seneca, and with Dr. Hines' efforts a sizable medical library was housed there. In 1938 at the session at Myrtle Beach the Association made acknowledgment of Dr. Hines' long and efficient services by presenting to him a silver service with suitable laudatory comment.

In this year the Greenville Society made a successful attempt at establishing voluntary nonprofit hospital insurance, the first of its kind in the state and forerunner of the Blue Cross Plan which was adopted some years later in 1947 by the whole Association. This was the year in which the American Medical Association was indicted as a trust, but came clear of the charges.

In 1939 the Association was represented at the celebration of the 150th anniversary of its parent society in Charleston, the Medical Society of South Carolina, and presented a bronze plaque in commemoration of the occasion.

Dr. Edgar Hines, secretary-treasurer-editor, died in 1940 and Dr. Julian Price succeeded him. A new medical publication appeared in the form of the *Bulletin* of the Anderson County Hospital, but its survival was not long.

The year 1941 saw rapid and effective activity on the part of the Procurement and Assignment Service in selecting the medical men of the state who were to enter the armed services. Pearl Harbor was attacked and preparation for a long and intensive war was accelerated. The difficult job of selecting the proper physicians for the military services and determining which should be left at home was conducted with eminent satisfaction and assiduity under the direction of Dr. W. L. Pressly, who had been president of the Association in 1941. In 1942, for his excellent work, the Association presented him a modest token of appreciation.

As in former times of war, the question arose as to how the practices and possessions of the absent doctors might be safe-guarded. A resolution was passed that those at home contribute to a pool one-fourth of their collections from the absent doctors' patients, but this plan did not work. In 1943 there were 286 doctors of South Carolina in the service and there was a relatively great shortage of physicians for civilians. Only one doctor was available in South Carolina for every 2,264 people.

Attempts to regiment and socialize medicine were becoming more frequent and insistent. The Wagner-Murray-Dingell bill with its broad provisions for regimentation received much attention and opposition from the profession throughout the country. South Carolina carried its share of antagonism to the proposal and her members worked through the National Physicians' Committee and otherwise to halt the progress of what they considered unsound "New Deal" legislation, and to offer more rational proposals for the improvement of medical care.

In 1943 the Association found that the many new developments in social and medical matters required a close observer and inter-preter. To keep itself abreast of affairs and to procure sound analy-sis and advice directly, the Association established the office of director of public relations, and secured an able executive in the person of Mr. M. L. Meadors of Florence, whose valuable services have continued to the present time.

A successful innovation of the same year was the inauguration of the three day "refresher courses" (later known as Postgraduate Seminars) at the Medical College. These courses were proposed, financed, and arranged by the Alumni Association of the Medical College, and proved very valuable and popular among the physicians of the state.

The rural districts were suffering from lack of medical care. A proposal by the Association that the state subsidize physicians who would give service in certain districts failed from lack of funds and lack of interested doctors. There was no immediate solution for the pressing difficulty.

The year 1944 saw the declaration of a Ten-Point Program aimed at circumventing or quashing the threat of political domination of the profession. The Association set up its aims in a "Ten-Point Program", as follows:

1. Cooperation

    To promote closer cooperation and better understanding between all groups and individuals concerned with providing and improving medical care for the people of South Carolina.

2. Political Control

    To prevent political control or domination of medical practice or of medical education.

3. Study

    To assemble and to amplify studies relative to the need and availability of medical care in each county of the state and in the state at large, and to publicize these findings.

    To study all agencies in the state which are involved in the administration of medical care as to the type of work which they are doing and the effectiveness of the work which is being done.

    To promote plans for providing or improving medical care where   there is a need.

4. Care of Indigent

    To prepare a uniform plan for the hospital care of the indigent, financed by public county funds, which may be used by individual counties or by groups of counties for their indigent sick, and to promote the general adoption of such a plan.

    To promote the establishments of clinics in each county for the indigent ambulatory patients, financed by public county funds, and operated or supervised by established hospitals or by the county medical society.

5. Hospital Insurance

    To make voluntary hospital insurance available to all the people of the state and to promote the widespread purchase of such insurance.

6. Hospitals

To study the present availability and facilities of hospitals in the state and to promote the establishment of well-equipped and adequately staffed hospitals in needy areas.

To establish through the State Medical Association standards for hospitals in South Carolina and to make public the names of those hospitals which meet these standards.

7. Group Health Insurance

To promote the establishment of group health insurance plans in all industries, large and small, in South Carolina.

8. Standards for Insurance

To establish standards for insurance companies selling hospital or group health insurance in South Carolina and to publish the names of those who meet these standards.

9. Medical and Nursing Education

To promote the securing of adequate funds and facilities for the operation of the Medical College of the State of South Carolina.

To promote advancement in nursing education and nursing in the state.

To promote the establishment of a loan fund whereby worthy young men and women of the state who are financially unable to meet the strain of a medical education may be able to secure aid.

10. Education of the Public

To acquaint the citizens of the state with regard to the agencies and facilities in the fields of medical care, public health, hospital and industrial insurance, and to encourage the people to use them on a much greater scale.

In 1944 activities of the State Board of Health were expanding with the approval and encouragement of the South Carolina Medical Association. A program for detection and control of rheumatic fever was set up in 1944.

The Association was well aware of the deficiencies in the supply of hospital beds in the state. At this time it was estimated that only about half of the desirable number of beds was available; in sixteen counties of South Carolina there was no hospital of any kind. As part of an effort toward improving the hospital services of the state and at the same time providing better teaching facilities, the Medical College began a successful movement for construction of the hospital which was to serve as a teaching unit for students. This move was supported enthusiastically by the Association.

Because of wartime conditions, no regular annual meeting was held in 1945. The Ten-Point Program continued to represent the chief objectives of the organization and contributions in some amount towards its goals were received from the membership. The Blue Cross Plan for hospital insurance, supported vigorously by the Association, finally passed the legislative hurdle in 1946.

Much discussion was held about this time about the status and location of the Medical College. A special "Committee of Seventeen" was appointed to investigate the condition and the needs of the school. It recommended that the college remain in Charleston and that all efforts of the Association should be made to bring about the necessary and desired improvements. An enlarged committee made heroic and successful efforts to push the passage of an act carrying a very large appropriation for this purpose.

In 1947 Dr. James McLeod devoted considerable effort to the development of the Woman's Auxiliary, realizing that it might serve as a potentially powerful factor in directing the public relations of the profession. The Association made an appropriation for the work of the Auxiliary and provided for the publication of a bulletin exclusively for the Auxiliary members.

The Association was much concerned in 1948 with the inaugural announcement of Governor Thurmond, who proposed to reorganize the State Board of Health and convert it into a lay board with minor medical representation. To combat this move, the Association set up a committee of its own which brought in recommendations for certain improvements in the activities of the Board without radical change. No change was made in the then current arrangement.

Membership had gone up to its record total of 1,012. The Association members were not happy with the activities of the naturopaths over the state. The Blue Shield Plan, chartered in 1949, was put into effect with 710 physicians as members and an arrangement whereby the House of Delegates of the Association served as the corporation for Blue Shield. A grievance committee was set up in 1952 to hear complaints on various aspects of medical practice.

In 1953 the Association carried out special efforts to obtain larger appropriations for the continuing construction of the Medical College Hospital. In the following year the Committee on Public Relations adopted an active program to improve the image of the doctor in the eyes of the public. Money was appropriated for the Historical Committee to prepare a history of medicine in South Carolina and work was begun immediately on this project. Also in 1953 Dr. Julian Price resigned as editor of the *Journal* and Dr. Joseph I. Waring assumed the editorial chair with the January issue of 1954.

In 1955 the total number of doctors in the state was 1,773, of whom 780 were general practitioners. Of these, 1,320 were members of the Medical Association.

After much maneuvering, in 1956, the law licensing naturopaths in the state was repealed. The Association took a very active part in abolishing this legislation.

In the meeting of 1957 there was some complaint about the way in which the Blue Shield was administered, but in spite of objections by a number of members, the operation of the plan was found to be in good condition. There was also concern about certain relations between the Medical College Hospital and the physicians of the state in the handling of patients, but amicable relations were soon restored. Dues were increased to include a portion for a permanent home fund.

At the request of the armed services, physicians of the state joined in promoting the successful operation of the original "Medicare", the program which was intended for families of men in the services. This was started in December 1957 and worked very successfully for a number of years. In 1958 the Association again had to gather its forces to fight the proposed national legislation in the form of the Forand Bill; the fight lasted on into 1960.

In 1959 a Benevolence Fund was established by the Association for the benefit of needy members of the profession. This move was accomplished by the efforts of Dr. W. Atmar Smith and the fund has continued to be active ever since. The Forand Bill for compulsory health insurance was still being debated in Congress and the Association continued in active opposition.

In 1959 the membership of the Association came to 1,482. In this year a Public Relations Program was initiated and resulted in production of television shows, speeches, addresses, and newspaper articles directed to the public. A system of reregistration of licenses with the Board of Medical Examiners was established. Civil Defense activities were promoted. While naturopathy had been out-lawed several years previously there was an effort in the state legis-lature to make exceptions which might make the law ineffective.

In 1964 a new program for furnishing medical information to the public through the columns of the newspapers was initiated by the Association and has continued to the present. It involved some 14 newspapers of the state, some of which publish the weekly articles regularly, others less frequently.

Growing concern in Congress with the development of federal programs for health measures of various kinds was reflected actively in the business of the Association. Ever since the time of Theodore Roosevelt proposals had been made to involve the government in provision of health care. The Wagner-Murray-Dingell bill, offered in 1943, had evoked strong resistance by the medical profession. The AMA and its members supported in 1948-49 a vigorous and extensive campaign against this measure. As a constituent society the South Carolina Medical Association was active in following the lead of its parent body. Efforts by Earl Warren to establish com-pulsory health insurance in California were made as early as 1945, and were defeated, but led to many other later proposals elsewhere.

In 1956 the Association spoke its opposition to the form of the proposed Forand Bill for hospital insurance for the aged. The same opposition was provided in South Carolina to the King-Anderson bills of 1960 and subsequent years, bills which proposed compulsory health insurance. However, the Kerr-Mills bill of 1961, which pro-vided grants to the states for old age assistance and for hospital care, met the approval of South Carolina physicians and became effective in the state in 1963.

A summation and modification of these various bills came in the proposal for the establishment of Medicare (1965) and later of Medicaid. The Association disapproved of the provisions of both of these measures and made futile objection to their implemen-tation. In 1967 the problem arose in proposal of Title XIX (or Medicaid) which appealed to the membership of the Association even less than had Medicare. The Association expressed serious disapproval of the measure but could accomplish nothing toward discouraging the passage of this legislation.

A long standing scarcity of physicians still obtained in the state, which could show only 77 doctors per 100,000 of population, com-pared to 146 as a national average. The few osteopaths of the state began at this time to make determined efforts to improve their status, and after several years of legislative campaigning finally achieved success in 1969, somewhat to the distress of the Medical Association, so that the osteopath is now licensed with the allopathic physician and has essentially the same privileges.

Educational television programs, which brought medical information and discussion to doctors and to the public over the state, were inaugurated. SCALPEL (now SOCPAC), a medical-political organization which operated independently of the State Association, was established and has continued to function. This year also saw an endorsement of the federal Regional Medical Program, which had begun in the previous year. Medicaid (Title XIX) achieved enabling legislation in 1968 and has continued to be a problem ever since.

In 1970 the shortage of physicians in South Carolina is critical. There are not only fewer physicians per unit of population but also the rate of increase of the number of physicians in the state has been less than the national rate. In 1968 there was a total of 2,137 physicians in South Carolina, including those in all medical activities, private, governmental, hospital-based, or in internship or residency. The rate of physicians actually furnishing patient care was 77 to 100,000 population. Rural South Carolina was far less properly supplied with physicians than were the metropolitan areas.

Increasing tendency toward the disappearance of the general practitioner or the family physician is a problem familiar to everyone. In 1963, 42 per cent of the non-governmental physicians providing patient care in the state were general practitioners. Five years later general practitioners represented only 34 per cent of physicians in active medical practice. Only 16 per cent of the medical graduates in South Carolina in the years 1965-67 entered general practice. Factors that have contributed to this decline are (1) tendency to specialization and research, (2) the harder work and lower pay of general practice, and (3) the emphasis on specialization which has been made in the past by the medical school faculties and the teaching hospitals. Growing concern with rebuilding family practice as a desirable type of life for the physician is giving some answer to these factors. The Medical University of South Carolina has established a department of family practice and a residency program in the newly recognized specialty. Spartanburg General Hospital has also established a residency in family practice. This healthy trend may do something to stop the downward progress of this very important division of medicine.

Under the able direction of Dr. William M. McCord, the Medical University has shaped a course toward encouraging an interest in general practice for its students, while at the same time it advances in its other branches of medicine.

✿   ✿   ✿   ✿   ✿   ✿

South Carolina medicine has advanced much in all respects since 1900, and promises a bright future.

THE PALMETTO MEDICAL, DENTAL, AND PHARMACEUTICAL ASSOCIATION

This organization for Negro physicians, dentists, and pharmacists, was organized in 1896 and has met annually. It was promoted largely by the efforts of Dr. C. C. Johnson of Columbia. It was divided at one time into three sections, the Piedmont, the Pee Dee, and the Congaree. These sections were scheduled to meet monthly and an annual three-day meeting of the whole association was arranged for the fourth Tuesday in April. The founders of the association were Drs. R. Levy of Florence, C. C. Johnson of Aiken, L. A. Earle of Anderson, and A. C. McClennan of Charleston.

The organization is now made up of four component societies, the Charleston County, the Congaree, the Piedmont, and the Inter-County, all of which have meetings monthly. Membership consists of about 50 physicians, about 50 dentists, and about 25 pharmacists.

CHAPTER 3

THE MEDICAL UNIVERSITY OF SOUTH CAROLINA

Except during the period of the War of the Confederacy, the Medical College of South Carolina had functioned since 1824 as a private proprietary institution, generally of high quality. In 1865 it raised itself from the ashes of war and went about its business, despite loss of faculty, equipment, and a general state of poverty, gradually resuming its full activity.

The year 1900 found it in very much the same state that it had endured for some years previous. It was still a privately operated school, blessed by the state with no more than a name, operating on a very small budget with a faculty composed entirely of volunteer part-time teachers. A faculty of eight members * and an adjunct faculty of twelve carried on the teaching. There were 43 graduates in 1900, a marked increase over the 20 of the year before.

The Flexner Report [1] on information obtained in February of 1909 gives a picture of the old Queen Street institution which must have applied pretty closely to that of 1900. It noted that entrance requirements were nominal, that total attendance was 213, and that there were 34 members of the teaching staff, none of whom was full-time. The financial resources of the college were based entirely on students' fees, which amounted to a total of something under $20,000. The latter part of the report read: "Laboratory facilities: Comprise very meager equipment for elementary chemistry, pharmacy, and anatomy—the dissecting-room in bad condition. The instructor in pathology and bacteriology has a fair private laboratory, to which students have no access; student work in those subjects is mostly confined to looking through the microscope at slides that he prepares. There is no museum, except old papier-maché and wax models, no library, except some antiquated publications. It is without other teaching aids. Clinical facilities: The school has access to the Roper Hospital, an unusually attractive institution of about 200 beds a mile distant. There were 80 patients at the time of the visit. Complaint is made that it is difficult to induce graduates to serve as internes. Obstetrical work is rare. There is no school or other organized dispensary."

---

* The professional faculty in 1900 consisted of F. L. Parker, E. F. Parker, John L. Dawson, J. Somers Buist, Manning Simons, P. G. de Saussure, Allard Memminger, and John Forrest.

[24]

Here then was a college of low rating, as compared to better known institutions, which could offer only limited instruction and limited opportunity for observation and experimentation. Prospects for improvement of the situation were dim.

In 1911 the college proposed that the University of South Carolina assume the operation of the school, but neither the university nor the college had much to offer to each other and nothing came of the proposal. Eventually and with some effort, largely that of Dr. Robert Wilson, who was to serve as dean for 35 years, the State of South Carolina was persuaded to assume operation and in 1913 the college became a state institution in fact, with an initial appropriation of $10,000. Almost at once it was rated as Class B, an improved but not yet adequate rating. The transfer to state operation was not without opposition from both Charleston and Columbia residents.

The struggle for funds was to continue. A new building was erected with private contributions of funds from Charleston without help from the state, and the college moved into its new home on Lucas (now Barre) Street. Gradually additional new buildings were added; the Physiology-Pharmacology Building in 1920, the Library-Pathology Building in 1930, the Outpatient Department in 1935 (partly from contributions by the alumni). The Simon Baruch Auditorium was built in 1940 with funds given by Mr. Bernard Baruch and in 1952 the Laboratory-Clinic Building completed the old quadrangle.

More important perhaps than the new buildings was the new faculty. The old faculty had consisted entirely of private practitioners up to 1913, when Dr. Kenneth Lynch came as professor of pathology. In 1915 Dr. W. F. R. Phillips assumed the chair of anatomy, and gradually additions to the full-time faculty occurred. Up to 1937 the faculty was still composed basically of private practitioners, generally untrained as teachers who gave their services with a variable degree of dedication and competence. After an absence of some years, Dr. Lynch returned in 1927 to his professorship of pathology. Now other full-time members of the faculty were added to the roster; Dr. John Boone and Dr. William Kelley in medicine, Dr. Frederick Kredel in surgery. In the 1940's the size of the classes was doubled. Roper Hospital served as the only teaching hospital for the school.

The course of the college was guided under many difficulties by the esteemed Dr. Robert Wilson. With the return of Dr. Kenneth Lynch, new and ambitious plans were prepared for improving the status of the school. Dr. Lynch acted in the capacity of vice dean and eventually was made dean, later becoming president and then chancellor of the college. The development of the physical and professional character of the present school is attributable very largely to his efforts.

In 1944 a determined movement for expansion of the college got under way, not without some opposition from some of both the Charleston and the Columbia medical professions, who saw the old ways going and viewed with suspicion a new arrangement. The legislature appropriated more generous funds for enlarging laboratories, and to crown the complex a teaching hospital of 500 beds was added in 1955. This final step allowed the removal of the probationary status in which the college had been for some time (since 1916) and brought certification as a full-fledged Class A institution. Actually full accreditation had been largely ensured in 1952 when the college admitted a class of 80 freshmen.

The Medical College Hospital came just in time to fill a vital need in teaching. Roper Hospital, a community hospital which had served as a teaching resource until 1944, found itself so lacking in funds from public sources that it was forced to give up the operation of its charity wards and outpatient department. A court order granted to the Medical Society of South Carolina (in Charleston) relief from the burden of operation of the charity services, which had long been vital adjuncts to the college. Roper Hospital managed to continue its outpatient department until 1948, but when Charleston County failed to appropriate sufficient funds for its operation this had to be closed, and the function was taken over by the Medical College. The new hospital afforded 500 beds for teaching purposes. While the private patients of Roper Hospital also continued as a resource, because of the unwillingness of that hospital to comply with certain federal regulations, it had to be eliminated from the field of teaching.

This was the beginning of the days of federal largesse. Grants became numerous, varied, and essential. The faculty grew, the curriculum expanded, property in the neighborhood of the college was acquired, and the college was on its way to a tremendous growth and improvement commensurate with a distinguished teaching institution.

Expansion of the plant proceeded steadily and capacity to accommodate a senior class of 80 students was achieved in 1960. Affiliation or association with adjacent institutions such as the Charleston County Hospital, the McClennan-Banks Hospital, and the Leon Banov Health Center of the Charleston County Health Department enlarged the area of student experience. In 1966 the new Veterans' Administration Hospital became an important part of the college's activity. In these various hospitals 1,200 or more beds became available and this increase in the opportunities for instruction allowed the enlargement of the capacity of the senior class to 102 members. The planned capacity for 1972 is 165.

As the Medical College gradually developed a group of disciplines outside of the strictly medical field, it comprised a complex of schools of nursing, pharmacy, dentistry, and allied health sciences, as well as the older graduate school of medicine, so that it became in effect a university. In 1969 the legislature recognized this status by changing the name from Medical College to Medical University.

As this book goes to press there is considerable discussion of a second medical school for the state, to be located in Columbia. This proposal has been pushed vigorously by most of the members of the Columbia profession. It has been opposed in Charleston and other areas and remains in an uncertain status. Dr. William M. McCord, president of the Medical University of South Carolina who has done so much to improve the condition of the medical school in Charleston, has stated that with expansion and better support of the present medical school all the needs of the state for medical practitioners can be readily met.

The history of the Medical University has been treated fully by Dr. Kenneth M. Lynch in *Medical Schooling in South Carolina 1823-1969*, published by the Alumni Association of the Medical College in 1970.[2]

REFERENCES

1. A. Flexner, *Medical Education in the United States and Canada.* A Report to the Carnegie Foundation for the Advancement of Teaching. Bulletin No. 4 (Boston, Updike 1910).

2. Kenneth M. Lynch, M.D., *Medical Schooling in South Carolina 1823-1969* (Columbia: R. L. Bryan Company 1970).

CHAPTER 4

PUBLIC HEALTH IN SOUTH CAROLINA AFTER 1900

THE STATE BOARD OF HEALTH

The 20th century was to see enormous improvements in public health. At its beginning progress was slow. Microbial causes of disease had been demonstrated only recently and the role of animal vectors just lately established. The carrier state in typhoid had been recognized by 1900. Only as recently as 1897 had the role of the mosquito in malaria been identified. Yellow fever, which harried the Carolina coast for many generations, had disappeared. So had cholera. Infant mortality, maternal mortality, morbidity from a long list of communicable diseases were all still excessively high. The state was beginning to assume greater responsibility for the public health and many volunteer organizations were about to wage intensive campaigns to reduce certain diseases.

Increasing knowledge of the basic facts of nutrition was beginning to show some results, though as late as 1916 pellagra was the second greatest cause of death in South Carolina. Industrial medicine was in its beginning in the state and health insurance was on its way, along with the rapid development of hospitals. The state had a very low per capita income and still retained its largely rural character. In the growth of cities new health problems were added to the many already demanding attention.

Through the efforts of the South Carolina Medical Association a State Board of Health had been established by an act passed December 21, 1878 and had begun to function in the following year. The entire membership of the state medical association was designated as the Board of Health. By the terms of the act seven elected officers of the Medical Association, along with the attorney general and the comptroller general, were named to make up an executive committee. According to the original act, their successors in office were to follow them on the board.

The Board of Health was designated as the sole advisor to the state on all questions involving protection of public health. In 1900, because of lack of funds, the activities of the board were very circumscribed. A budget of $15,000 a year did not allow a very effective performance. The local boards of health established some years previously were supposedly supervised by the State Board but because of lack of concern, of funds, and personnel the efficacy of the supervision was minor. The control of communicable disease was still the chief function of the board and involved quarantine measures and the single available prophylactic practice of vaccination against smallpox. The diseases which chiefly engaged attention were smallpox, the enteric fevers, malaria, scarlet fever, typhus, tuberculosis, and diphtheria.

The annual report of the State Board of Health for the fiscal year 1900 gives some idea of its activities. There was some concern with building inspection. It was noted that smallpox, relatively mild, had been prevalent for the preceding three years. Among other problems, the extensive amount of pellagra in the state was stressed. The board recommended the employment of a bacteriologist and stated that the quarantine stations at Georgetown, St. Helena, and Port Royal, all operated by the state, apparently were not justified by the amount of current shipping. It also took notice of the pollution of the rivers of South Carolina and reported that it had carried out its designated function of inspecting the state's charitable and penal institutions. It remarked that the 37 existing county boards of health were not in close relation with the central State Board and rather resented the supervision and advice offered by that body.

In 1905 the Board of Health succeeded in having a law passed requiring vaccination against smallpox, still in occasional epidemic proportion. This measure was accomplished largely through the requirement that all children be vaccinated before admission to school. In the following year 41 physicians were designated as temporary official vaccinators over the various areas of the state.

In 1907 a statute required every water company, public or private, to have chemical and bacteriological analyses made.

Pellagra was attracting more attention, to the extent that an International Pellagra Conference was called in Columbia in 1908. Much later the State Board of Health participated extensively in the campaign to eliminate the disease by distributing brewer's yeast to supplement defective diets and by educating the people in dietary knowledge.

The original and succeeding acts concerning the State Board of Health made no provision for an administrative head, until the act of 1908 created the office of a state health officer, who was to carry out the purposes of the board under the direction of the executive committee. Dr. C. Frederick Williams was the first to hold this office, with a salary of $2,500. One of the first of his many measures for improvement of the efficiency of the board was the creation of a bacteriological laboratory in 1909. After Dr. Williams' short term of three years, he was succeeded in 1912 by Dr. James A. Hayne who continued in office until 1944, when Dr. Ben F. Wyman succeeded him. In 1954 he was succeeded by Dr. G. S. T. Peeples whose place was taken in January 1967 by Dr. Kenneth Aycock, the present incumbent.

In 1908 diphtheria and typhoid fever occupied much of the board's concern. Antitoxin was provided to combat diphtheria and later diphtheria toxin-antitoxin and eventually toxoid were distributed by the State Health Department. At this time the large amount of typhoid fever demanded attention by way of vaccination and serious concern with sanitary improvement, including considerable interest in the construction of rural privies. The Hygienic Laboratory was created in 1909 to provide diagnostic and therapeutic aid.

In 1906 all the quarantine stations previously operated by the state were transferred to the federal government and the power of quarantine enforcement on shipping was placed in its hands. The state continued to control internal quarantine regulations.

In 1910 communicable disease was the chief concern of the State Board of Health. The sale of food and drugs came under its eye in 1913 and in 1914 the Bureau of Vital Statistics was set up. In the next year the South Carolina Tuberculosis Sanatorium was erected under the board's direction.

Following this year considerable attention was given to local health services. With the help of generous grants from the Rockefeller Foundation, the first county health departments in South Carolina were established in Greenwood and Orangeburg counties. By 1926, some 24 counties were employing full time health officers, nurses, and clerical helpers.

The widespread prevalence of hookworm in the state had been detected as early as 1902. In the period of 1912-1914 the Rockefeller Sanitary Commission provided means whereby a statewide survey of the rural areas could be made. The report of this study indicated that 37.3% of the large number of persons examined showed the presence of the ova of hookworm. In some areas the percentage of positives ran up as high as 77.5% (Georgetown) and 74.6% (Berkeley), largely in the barefoot population. A number of other counties approached these figures.

In later years, a sampling survey made in 1936 in 557 communities in the rural areas all over the state showed that the incidence of hookworm infestation was much lower, but still was at 24.8%. The greater contribution to this figure was from the eastern section (29.3%), as compared to the western area (4.7%). The greatest incidence was in the group of persons from 5 to 19 years. A survey of a relatively small number of Negroes was made and showed only 7% were positive in the single sample. The surveyors also noted that 34.2% of the houses inspected had no facilities for excreta disposal, a commentary on the sanitary conscience of the state.[1]

Recognizing the work of the State Board of Health and realizing its need for increased authority, the legislature in 1912 gave it quasi-legislative powers which allowed it to make and enforce regulations necessary to the control of disease.

The incidence of a number of diseases has been enormously reduced in the state since 1900. Scarlet fever prevailed in the piedmont area in 1907-1908. One of the periodic appearances of dengue came to the coast in 1919. Diphtheria was abundant in Greenville in 1942, typhus in 1940. Smallpox continued to be active in the early part of the century, but had disappeared by 1930. Tuberculosis, "captain of the men of death", was far less prevalent, and many prognosticators saw the end of this scourge and even went so far as to say that tuberculosis sanitariums would no longer be necessary. The fact that 630 cases were reported in 1969 seems to indicate that there was premature rejoicing over the disappearance of the disease. Typhoid fever was the source of many deaths in the earlier 1900's. In 1925 it was responsible for 448 deaths in South Carolina; in 1969 only one case was reported. The diarrheal diseases have retreated to far lower numbers, and hookworm disease, while it has not disappeared, has been reduced very extensively. One of the more spectacular achievements of the period was the eradication of malaria in the state as a result of drainage, screening, and use of pesticides and drugs. A case of malaria in South Carolina now is obviously imported.

Pellagra, recognized as a serious problem early in the century and a major cause of death, showed 3,379 cases as late as 1932 and 310 deaths in 1935. It has now decreased to a very small number of cases, all of which are entirely preventable. Syphilis has had its ups and downs, with a varying prevalence, but still supplies an undesirable segment of our morbidity. Poliomyelitis, which had afflicted the state in several severe epidemics over the period, has become a rarity as a result of many factors, principally the use of the specific vaccine.

Dengue fever produced 34 cases in 1934, the last outbreak of any size in the state. Filariasis, a disease limited almost entirely to the Carolina low country, has apparently disappeared. Diphtheria has plummeted from a very high level to a total report of 3 cases in 1969 as compared with 682 reported cases in 1945. The development of adequate immunizing procedures is obviously responsible for most of this gain.

Health officials and others are aware of the fact that the practitioner is not always too conscientious in reporting his cases, but the trends in morbidity figures are obvious. Some of the improvement was the result of general progress in hygiene and sanitation, some of it due to specific and vigorous direct efforts by official and non-official organizations. To offset somewhat this gratifying decrease in the diseases that afflicted the state in the first half of the century, there has been an increase in certain other conditions, perhaps not sufficient to balance the gain in the disappearance of the group mentioned above.

The ailments which now occupy the forefront of the public health problem in the state are commonly recognized but are not adequately controlled by our present means. Cancer has risen high in the scale; heart disease, a condition to which South Carolinians seem to be rather unusually subject, has increased to an unhappy extent. Hepatitis is now a rather common disorder seldom seen in earlier years. Rheumatic fever has increased, or at least has been recognized more often by more adequate diagnostic measures. Cases of septic sore throat still occur in large numbers, varying from year to year, and still are too common. Similarly, influenza continues to come in epidemics of various size and seriousness. New forms of the influenza virus develop with some regularity and permanent protection is seldom obtainable. The great epidemic of 1918-1919, characterized as the "greatest medical holocaust in history", probably was the worst in the medical annals of South Carolina. It affected 10 per cent of the population and produced between 4,000 and 5,000 deaths in the state out of a total of probably 150,000 to 170,000 cases.

A considerable addition to the armament of the State Board of Health was the development of the Bureau of Child Hygiene in 1919. The problem of supervision of the more than 1,000 midwives registered in the state came under this activity. The year 1922 brought increased funds from the federal government through the Sheppard-Towner Act and allowed much expansion of activity. In 1928 pellagra was attacked vigorously by means of the distribution of many tons of brewer's yeast.

The hard times of 1930-1935 had their effect on the whole program of the State Board of Health. The rural sanitation and county health work lost 60 per cent of its former income and funds and personnel were drastically reduced. The Social Security Act of 1935 allowed restoration and expansion of the previous activity. In 1947 Gov. Thurmond proposed a move to change the composition of the State Board of Health so as to reduce drastically the medical representation and serious consideration was given to his plan. A special study by Dr. Harry Mustard at the behest of the South Carolina Medical Association offered proposals to soften the blow. No change was made.

Over the years the executive committee of the Board of Health has been enlarged by the addition of a pharmacist, a dentist, a nurse, and a veterinarian. In 1969, the status of the Board of Health was again threatened by the efforts of Gov. McNair to effect a merger of the Department of Health and the Department of Welfare and to eliminate medical membership and influence on the proposed controlling board. The question remains unsettled.

During the twentieth century the growth and accomplishments of the State Board of Health have been rather extraordinary. A continuing increase in funds, both state and federal, and in competent personnel has allowed great expansion and coordination. Similar developments in county health departments have produced parallel increases in efficiency and in scope. The interest of the State Board and the county boards have been identical.

The phases of public health now included in the programs are very numerous. How broad the concern is may be gathered from a long list of the various projects of the State Board of Health, which carries on activities in epidemiology, tuberculosis control, venereal disease control, geriatrics, crippled children, drug inspection, vital statistics, bedding inspection, water pollution control, public water supply inspection and sewerage disposal, laboratories, cancer control, heart disease control, veterinary public health, ma-

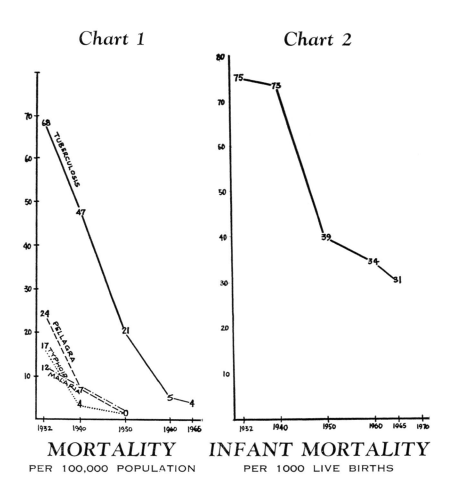

Chart 1

Chart 2

MORTALITY
PER 100,000 POPULATION

INFANT MORTALITY
PER 1000 LIVE BIRTHS

ternal and child health, dental health, hospital construction and licensing, insect and rodent control, food processing, retail food, hotels, trailer parks, organized camps, milk, shellfish, bottling plants, frozen desserts, and public health education.

REFERENCE

1. W. S. Leathers, A. E. Keller, and B. F. Wyman, "State-wide Investigation of Hookworm in South Carolina," *Amer. J. Hyg.*, 23:600 (May 1936).

CHARLESTON BOARDS OF HEALTH

The Board of Health of the City of Charleston extends well back to the middle of the 19th century. In 1880 it was reorganized with Dr. Robert Lebby as registrar and Dr. H. B. Horlbeck as clerk, who had offices in the old City Hospital on Mazyck Street. Dr. Horlbeck became secretary, later health officer, was at one time president of the American Public Health Association, and was active in efforts to control yellow fever nationally. He did a great deal in Charleston toward establishing a proper sewerage system. Largely through his efforts the flush toilet became a generally accepted piece of Charleston furniture.

In 1901 Dr. J. Mercier Green was made health officer and served for a few years. Dr. F. L. Frost held the office in 1905-1906 and Dr. H. W. deSaussure served for a few months. Dr. Green then returned to his position and pursued an active course in bettering the health affairs of the city. He was particularly interested in studies of the prevalent typhoid fever and on methods of eliminating sources of the disease. He also was efficient in accomplishing the removal of a large number of cows who inhabited the city. In 1909 and 1910 Dr. Green made special efforts to improve the sewerage of the city, and established the system of food inspection which proved very advantageous. Dr. G. McF. Mood gave long and competent service to the Health Department in the capacity of bacteriologist. Dr. Leon Banov made a name for himself as a very efficient assistant to Dr. Green and worked successfully on improving milk inspection and later on the establishment of pasteurization of milk in the city. The ordinance which required pasteurization is thought to have been the first of its kind anywhere.

In May 1920, with the assistance of funds from the Rockefeller Foundation, which was particularly interested in the local prevalence of intestinal parasites, the Charleston County Health Department was established with Dr. Banov as health officer. In 1926 Dr. Banov began to serve as health officer in a dual capacity for both city and county. In 1936 the city Board of Health was terminated and the Charleston County Board of Health was established. It concerned itself through the Health Department with reduction of infant mortality, immunization, establishment of well baby clinics, and the development of a tuberculosis sanatorium (Pinehaven). In the last named effort Dr. Banov was particularly active and successful. The Health Department at that period had its offices in the Old Citadel.

Certain disgruntled politicians were anxious to replace Dr. Banov and to control the Board of Health. After a period of unpleasantness they were convinced that the operation of the board was competent and honest.

Following World War II there was an active campaign to reduce the typhus fever which was prevalent in the city.

In 1961 Dr. Banov retired and was succeeded in turn by Dr. Kenneth Aycock, Dr. Lucius P. Varn, Dr. Malcolm Dantzler, and Dr. Cecil Jacobs, who carried on from the excellent foundation made during Dr. Banov's tenure of office.

The Charleston County Health Department is now housed in two separate buildings adjacent to the Charleston County Hospital.

COLUMBIA PUBLIC HEALTH ACTIVITIES

A Columbia Board of Health was established as early as 1825, reorganized in 1878, and still continues to function, although many of its activities have been taken over by the Richland County Board of Health established in 1935. Dr. William Boyd was the first health officer for the city, and worked particularly to provide better sewer connections at a time when there were still a great many surface privies in the city. In 1917 a cooperative arrangement was made with the United States Public Health Service to provide health measures in the city for the soldiers from Fort Jackson, particularly during an epidemic of meningitis in that year. A number of patients were treated in the Riverside Hospital, the old pest house on the Broad River Road.

In 1918, Dr. Skottowe Fishburne was health officer, but later resigned his position, as did Dr. Jean LaBorde, in 1924. Dr. Fishburne was succeeded by Dr. M. M. Rice, and later by Dr. R. T. Jennings. In 1930 Dr. Eugene Payne assumed the position, but died in 1942. He was followed in turn by Mr. Gresham Caughman, a pharmacist, and Dr. William Pitts (1947-1950). The latter was succeeded by Dr. Charles Sloan, who remains in office. For a brief time Dr. James Watson substituted for him. These officers were all on part-time status.

Efforts by the Columbia Medical Society to have the city and county departments merged have not been successful. The two organizations carry on parallel activities, not conflicting.

Columbia's water supply was furnished privately by Col. Abram Blanding as early as 1819 and was sold to the city in 1835. In 1935, the year in which the County Health Department was established, great improvements were made in the water system with the help of federal funds. Sewerage disposal still continues to be a problem.

REFERENCE

Owens, Frank C., M.D., *City of Columbia Board of Health, 1964.* MS in City of Columbia office of the Board of Health.

GREENVILLE COUNTY DEPARTMENT OF HEALTH

The Greenville County Health Department was established by Act 390 of the state legislature February 25, 1914. It was located in the County Courthouse and an adjacent frame building in 1943 when the increased demand for services and space by four selective service boards in the county, the establishment of an air base by the Army and a glider training school necessitated applying for War Public Works grant to renovate a building to house the department. At that time, the staff was increased from 18 to 33, and the department was carrying on programs in communicable disease control, venereal disease control, tuberculosis control, maternity service, infant and preschool care, school hygiene (including dental work), crippled children, providing laboratory services for the clinics, sanitation services including water and sewage, garbage disposal, insect control, food control, milk supply, and summer camp inspection. The 1940 population for the county was 136,580.

The present health center was completed in March 1966, at which time the staff numbered almost 50. Since that time, again because of increased demands for services (resulting from growing population, expanded programs and new programs), the building has been altered to provide more clinic space and more suitably arranged office space. This center now houses more than 90 persons, including staff members, State Board of Health personnel assigned to the area, and project personnel for several funded projects. In addition to the standard public health programs, the department also provides home health services, family planning, both environmental and clinical laboratory services, social service, vital statistics, and a maternity and infant care project which encompasses pre-natal and post-partum care for high risk mothers and baby screen-ing and child health conferences for their infants. A recent addi-tion to this project is a pediatric-obstetric clinic for pregnant teenagers (16 and under). Another project in operation is the air pollution control program, which has established a network of monitoring stations and effects stations in the county and is in the process of conducting an emission survey at the present time.

The dental health program and the health educator corps pro-gram, which have been approved for the Appalachian Region, will involve this county and this agency.

SPARTANBURG COUNTY HEALTH DEPARTMENT

A County Health Department was established in 1925 with offices in the Harris Building on the Square, and afterwards moved to the old Becker residence, later to the General Hospital, then to 891 N. Church St., and finally in 1942 to a new building provided with federal funds. Originally named the Department of Health and Hospital operations, it was designated as the County Health Department, with Dr. Hilla Sheriff as health officer. Later Dr. David Garvin, Dr. John O. Setzler, and Dr. James Brabham served as health officers. In 1951 Dr. J. C. Hedden took charge of Spar-tanburg and Cherokee Counties. Under his administration there were many improvements; establishment of the Visiting Nurses Association, extension of the clinic wing, an office wing addition, and the setting up of six auxiliary centers located at Landrum, Chesnee, Woodruff, Cowpens, Inman, and Duncan. In 1960 the Spartanburg City Health Department was consolidated with the County Health Department. A new building at 151 East Wood St. was constructed in 1968 with funds from the Hill-Burton Act and now houses 48 people. The department at that time operated with an annual budget of $342,000.

Among the special public health activities was the establishment of a cancer clinic in 1934 and a health council in 1941. A tubercu-losis hospital was built in 1942 under a separate board.

In 1943 the County Health Department was awarded an honor certificate by the American Public Health Association. Many other activities commonly performed now in health departments were added as time passed. Special campaigns against syphilis, polio, and other older problems in communicable disease have been car-ried out at various times.

CHAPTER 5

THE COUNTY MEDICAL SOCIETIES

Excepting a few of the larger societies of the state, the county medical societies offer few records on which to base a description of their careers. Many of the smaller societies have no records, and recollections from some of the older members are sometimes of dubious accuracy. Nevertheless, an effort has been made to compile information on as many of those organizations as available data allow.

At the time of the inception of the South Carolina Medical Association, the state was divided into district societies, not corresponding to the present day district societies in territory or activity. At the organizational meeting in Charleston in 1848 there were delegates from only five district societies, namely Charleston, Orangeburg, Chester, York, and Georgetown. In 1853 Colleton District was added. The Pee Dee Medical Association was apparently a component part of the Association, or at least it reported its activities to that body. In 1869 the development of county medical societies was promoted by the Association and four years later the current list included Abbeville, Edgefield, Greenville, Kershaw, Orangeburg, Charleston, Columbia, Anderson, and Newberry. Other counties soon followed. In 1891 Greenville and Sumter county societies were chartered and in 1892 charters were granted to the Georgetown and Florence societies. It was reported at the annual meeting of the South Carolina Medical Association in 1892 that the Barnwell County Medical Society had been in existence over two years. By 1906 all of the counties then in existence except Berkeley, Chesterfield, and Lancaster were organized and affiliated with the South Carolina Medical Association. Among those participating were Lexington (chartered in 1885), Marlboro (1897), Oconee (1903), Pickens (1890), and Spartanburg. This last society (the city society of 1866) was chartered as a county society in 1901.

While a number of these societies were nominally properly organized and active, their participation in the business of the Association was not always consistent. At the meeting in Charleston in 1900, the 50th anniversary meeting, delegates were present from Charleston, Kershaw, Greenville, Anderson, Florence, Sumter,

Union, Lancaster, and the Pee Dee. At that time the total membership of the Association was in the neighborhood of 300 out of about 1,100 practitioners in the state.

Reorganizational activities in the American Medical Association about this time were predicated partly on the desire to make the county society the basic unit of medical organization. A concerted effort was made to promote formation and reorganization of county societies throughout the country. In South Carolina this movement took place in 1905 and 1906, when a special representative from the AMA traveled the state endeavoring to awaken interest in county organization and function. As a result of this effort, there was a very definite improvement in the activities of these groups with a consequent enlivening of the work of the state Association.

In 1970 counties with organized medical societies were Abbeville, Aiken, Allendale, Anderson, Barnwell, Beaufort, Berkeley, Charleston, Cherokee, Chester, Chesterfield, Colleton, Darlington, Dillon, Dorchester, Fairfield, Florence, Georgetown, Greenville, Greenwood, Hampton, Horry, Kershaw, Lancaster, Laurens, Marion, Marlboro, Newberry, Oconee, Pickens, Richland (Columbia Medical Society), Spartanburg, Union, Williamsburg, and York. Bamberg, Calhoun, and Orangeburg counties are united in the Edisto Medical Society, Edgefield, Saluda, and portions of Lexington counties form the Ridge Medical Society, and Sumter and Clarendon are joined in the Sumter-Clarendon Medical Society. There are no organized societies in Jasper, Lee, and McCormick counties.

The information given in the following brief summaries of the histories of the county medical societies has been obtained partially from reports from the societies themselves, partially from information in the various older directories of the American Medical Association, and from references from the *Journal of the South Carolina Medical Association*. In many cases the information obtained is very scanty, but it appears to be all that is available at this time.

ABBEVILLE COUNTY MEDICAL SOCIETY

A medical society was founded in Abbeville in 1835. An application for a charter was made to the South Carolina Medical Association in 1855. At that time it had 25 members. Again this society must have languished for it was reorganized in 1870 and again in 1878. It was organized once more in the early 1900's by Drs. G. A. Neuffer, L. T. Hill, F. E. Harrison, and C. C. Gambrell, and became affiliated with the South Carolina Medical Association by September 1905 with 14 members. The society has always been relatively small in membership.

AIKEN COUNTY MEDICAL SOCIETY

The Aiken County Medical Society was organized in 1905. In 1906 it had 25 members. It continued with more or less activity for some time until it was reorganized in 1925. Again it seems to have fallen into inactivity and was revived in 1938 with Dr. Paul Culbreath as the president. It was incorporated September 21, 1963. There are now 34 active members of the society. Dr. James DeLoach is president.

ALLENDALE COUNTY MEDICAL SOCIETY

Allendale became a new county of the state and its society applied for a charter in 1919. The first listing as a component society of the South Carolina Medical Association is in the AMA Directory of 1921 which shows that Dr. H. G. Googe was president and Dr. J. S. Palmer was secretary. During the 1930's Allendale County joined with Barnwell and Hampton counties to form the Savannah Valley Medical Society. By 1940 it was a single society again. Dr. W. R. Tuten, Sr. was president and Dr. A. B. Preacher was secretary-treasurer. There were four members in 1949. The society is affiliated with the 8th District Society. It reported only three members in 1969.

ANDERSON COUNTY MEDICAL SOCIETY

By 1900 the medical society organized in Anderson in the latter part of the 19th century had disappeared. In 1906 reorganization was effected with 23 members. Dr. Frank Lander was elected president. The society did not follow a very active course though it did meet occasionally, often at the Court House, with a luncheon meeting at the local hotel. Programs were rather scanty, rarely being graced with outside speakers.

In the period of 1920-1930 meetings became more regular and the programs were improved. In 1930 the society joined with the Anderson County Tuberculosis Association in promoting a tuberculosis hospital in Anderson County, but this was never accomplished. The Calhoun Hotel was a meeting place until about 1930, when the custom of meeting at the Anderson Memorial Hospital was inaugurated.

BAMBERG COUNTY MEDICAL SOCIETY

Bamberg County Medical Society was organized in 1905 and became affiliated with the South Carolina Medical Association by

April 1906 with 12 members. It became a part of the Edisto Medical Society in the early 1930's.

BARNWELL COUNTY MEDICAL SOCIETY

The Medical Society of Barnwell District was established in 1832 or perhaps earlier. A fee bill was published in 1841. In 1892 at a meeting of the South Carolina Medical Association in Georgetown, it was reported that the Barnwell society had been in existence "over two years", held quarterly meetings, and had 30 members. It became an affiliate society of the SCMA by September 1905, but with only seven members listed. For a short time Barnwell and Hampton counties joined together in one society. Then, in the 1930's Barnwell, Allendale, and Hampton counties formed the Savannah Valley Medical Society. Barnwell County Medical Society was inactive during the 1940's but was listed again as a component society in the AMA Directory of 1956.

BEAUFORT COUNTY MEDICAL SOCIETY

During the period of medical organization of the counties a Beaufort Society was established in 1906 with seven members. Although it was listed in the AMA directories through 1921, it apparently had little or no activity.

According to the AMA Directory of 1929, Beaufort and Jasper counties joined together to form the Beaufort-Jasper Medical Society with Dr. Van Smith, president and Dr. H. B. Senn, secretary. Prior to that time there had never been anything but a loose organization of physicians in the area. The Beaufort society continued under this double name for many years, but reverted to its original separate name in the late 1950's or early 1960's.

For some time this society held a business meeting once yearly. Scientific and social meetings were held bimonthly through membership in the Coastal Medical Society. It now meets regularly with the Beaufort County Memorial Hospital staff.

BERKELEY COUNTY MEDICAL SOCIETY

No records can be found on the early activities of the Berkeley County Medical Society. It was not included in the counties reorganized in 1905 and 1906 under the auspices of the AMA and the SCMA. According to the AMA Directory, it was a component society in 1929, when Dr. G. S. T. Peeples of Bonneau was secretary.

CALHOUN COUNTY MEDICAL SOCIETY

Calhoun County was established in 1908. The first record of the Calhoun County Medical Society is in the AMA Directory of 1914 which lists it with Orangeburg County. It is listed as a separate society in the AMA Directory of 1916, with Dr. L. B. Bates, president, and Dr. T. H. Symmes, secretary. It was dropped from the list of component societies in the 1920's and in the 1930's it joined with Orangeburg and Bamberg counties to form the Edisto Medical Society.

CHARLESTON
(THE MEDICAL SOCIETY OF SOUTH CAROLINA)

In 1900 Dr. R. B. Rhett was president of the Medical Society of South Carolina, formed in 1789. The society consisted of about 40 members with an average attendance of 15. The membership of the time was concerned with water, both internal and external, inasmuch as it took occasion to discuss the drinking water supply of the city and also to promote private bathing pavilions on the waterfront. It was recommended that these latter structures be put on the east side at Vardelle Creek, at the foot of Society Street, and North Adger's Wharf, on the west end of Tradd Street, Halsey's Mill, and Gadsden Green. As a result of the interest of the society, the city was induced to appropriate money to carrying out the proposal, but only at the Society Street site.

The society had an active and fairly extensive library which had evolved from the donation of books as far back as the 18th century. The library subscribed to a number of journals and also purchased a few books from time to time and received frequent donations from the members. In 1899 it had a part-time librarian and was available to the students at the Medical College.

In November of 1900 the society took cognizance of the fact that tuberculous patients were admitted into the general wards of City Hospital and begged for a separate ward. It concerned itself too with the efforts of the students of the Medical College of the State of South Carolina to secure exemption from examination before the State Medical Examiners Board. After much discussion a resolution by Dr. L. D. Barbot that the society endorse the bill was passed and forwarded to the legislature.

Once more an effort at local sanitation was to be seen in the passage of a motion to secure cuspidors for the Medical Society's hall. Later in the year the society granted to the Board of Health permission to use rooms in the old Queen Street (Roper) Hospital for reception of contagious diseases, as an annex to City Hospital. In 1903 a standing committee on sanitation was created.

In 1904 the physical condition of City (Memorial) Hospital was reported to be very poor and it was also noted that it had never been a properly constructed building. The society requested City Council to allow the use of the accumulated Roper Fund and the municipal appropriation for the City Hospital to promote the rehabilitation and improvement of the building. A committee on rebuilding was appointed and a resolution was made to sell the old damaged Roper Hospital structure on Queen Street. After an agreement with the City Council May 21, 1904, in 1906 the new hospital was completed and put back under the management of the society.

A new constitution was adopted October 1, 1904, and a new charter from the South Carolina Medical Association was received June 22, 1905. Dr. Robert Wilson offered plans for an anti-tuberculosis league and application was made for a charter for the Roper Hospital Training School for Nurses. A "blacklist" of financially delinquent patients was popular with the membership.

On February 1, 1907 Dr. C. W. Kollock announced that the Charleston Medical School (a summer school conducted by the society) was to disband and the South Carolina Postgraduate Medical School was to be organized within the facilities of Roper Hospital. In May the society decided to form instead its own Polyclinic School of Medicine and Surgery of the Roper Hospital and elected professors to the chairs. In December 1907 Dr. C. P. Aimar, president of the faculty, reported seven pupils.

Continuing to receive donations of books from various sources, the society built its library up to a total of some 8,000 volumes. In December 1908 the Polyclinic had 17 students. Earlier, on June 1, 1907, funds from the old South Carolina Training School for Nurses (chartered in 1883 at the City Hospital) had been transferred to the Roper Hospital Training School Home for Nurses. It lasted only long enough to graduate two classes, then lost the support of City Council. A nurses home known as the R. A. Kinloch Home was built with donations from the Medical Society and the citizens of Charleston and was occupied August 5, 1910.

In 1913 the society was active in raising funds for the new Medical College building. The Polyclinic Summer Medical School was dissolved in 1913. There was still much interest in the library. Upon the request of Dr. Lynch the books were loaned to the Medical College for the use of students and faculty. Later, after the books were returned to the Medical Society, a number of them were sent on loan to the surgeon general's library where they remained for some time and were eventually returned intact.

The Thompson bequest of $55,000 was received in 1915. Various bequests were made before and after this time. Among them was the Murray Memorial building, gift to the city of the family of Andrew Murray, later transferred to the ownership of the hospital. In April 1924, the Woman's Auxiliary to the society was formed.

In 1932 times were hard and city warrants were in use. Roper Hospital developed a deficit and the city was in arrears. In tune with financial affairs, in January 1933 the society reduced its dues from $15 to $10 and in the next year proposed a credit bureau.

In 1935 a medal awarded to Dr. T. G. Simons by the Howard Association in Memphis was presented to the society with the family of Dr. Simons present. On March 25 a credit bureau was getting under way. On April 9 a report was made on the status of the proposed Ross Museum and the Medical Society's interest in the Ross estate was explained.

Because of insufficient collection the credit bureau was abandoned in the spring of 1935. On October 8 a resolution approving the establishment of a birth control clinic was passed and in 1937 funds were obtained through the generosity of Victor Morawetz, who also gave funds for building an isolation unit for Negroes. In October the credit bureau was revived. In November a proposal was made to raise dues to $15 to make the finances of the society adequate and the offices of secretary and treasurer were combined.

The society declined an invitation by the local radio stations to take part in a public education program, but relented a little later. At this time the firm of Hagood, Rivers, and Young was appointed attorneys of the society. On February 11, 1936, WPA workers were engaged in copying the old minutes of the society.

During 1936 Dr. Waring, librarian, obtained permission to sell certain books and duplicates in the library. The society accepted the offer of Mrs. Joseph Hume to donate the medical library of the late Dr. Joseph Hume. The credit bureau was active.

In 1939 the society celebrated its sesquicentennial year with proper ceremony, including a banquet with an historical address by Dr. F. B. Packard of Philadelphia, a luncheon, and exhibits of medical historical material at the Gibbes Art Gallery. The president-elect of the American Medical Association and representatives of other medical societies were in attendance.

Negotiations for obtaining a grant and loan from the federal government were pursued for some time and, on April 20, 1943, culminated in a substantial appropriation to be used to construct the new Roper Hospital. The old plant was partially abandoned when the new structure was completed.

In 1951 the society began publication of *The Scribe*, a bulletin with state-wide circulation. In this year steps were taken toward the formation of the Charleston County Medical Society. The Medical Society of South Carolina continued as a corporate body with its chief interest in Roper Hospital and in November the charter of the older society was surrendered to the South Carolina Medical Association. The county society then assumed the activity related to the state medical organization.

In September an invitation to the Negro physicians of the community to practice in Roper Hospital was declined. All indebtedness of the Roper Hospital to the federal government was discharged in this year; and in 1953 the Victor Morawetz bequest was received and expansion of the hospital was planned.

In 1956 the books of the library were moved to quarters in the library of the Medical College on the basis of an indefinite loan. A provision was made that they were not to leave Charleston.

On November 19, 1959, the old Roper Hospital plant was closed and the emergency room was transferred to the administration of the Medical College. In the next year the Thompson Memorial Building and the Kinloch Home were demolished. Later the Lucas Home (Riverside Infirmary) was renovated and property was purchased on the southwest corner of Barre and Calhoun Streets.

In July 1965, since Roper Hospital was not in compliance with federal regulation, it became necessary to abandon all medical student training which had been given from time immemorial to the Medical College. State agency contracts were discontinued and questions of integration were agitated. The society decided not to participate in the Medicare program.

The old Roper Hospital building was demolished in 1966, marking the end of a period of 60 years of community and educational service.

Roper Hospital continues to grow as a well accepted community hospital. It now receives Negro patients and offers a wide variety of services to the Charleston area.

REFERENCE

Joseph I. Waring, M.D., *A Brief History of Roper Hospital* (Charleston: Published by the Board of Commissioners of Roper Hospital, 1964).

CHARLESTON COUNTY MEDICAL SOCIETY

The Charleston County Medical Society, founded in 1951, is a lineal descendant of the first permanent medical society of the state, the Medical Society of South Carolina. This older society was established in Charleston in 1789 with a view to developing a state-wide membership. It later became one of the component district societies which made up the South Carolina Medical Association in 1848.

When the districts of the state were divided into counties, it assumed the status of a county society. In this capacity it continued to function until 1951, when it decided to limit its activity to administration of the affairs of the Roper Hospital. The society then surrendered its charter as a county unit of the South Carolina Medical Association, thereby making room for the immediate formation of the Charleston County Medical Society, which was new in name but essentially a continuation of the older organization as a unit of the state Association.

The Charleston County Medical Society meets regularly ten times a year.

CHEROKEE COUNTY MEDICAL SOCIETY

The Cherokee County Medical Society became affiliated with the South Carolina Medical Association by September 1905 with a membership of 13 members. It continued as an active component society, although the records of the society itself are non-existent.

CHESTER COUNTY MEDICAL SOCIETY

This was originally a district society of variable activity since its orgin in 1849. It applied for a charter as a county society in 1883. It was reorganized in April 1904 during the organization program by the American Medical Association, directed by Dr. J. N. McCormack. The officers elected at this meeting were Dr. S. G. Miller, president, and Dr. W. B. Cox, secretary-treasurer.

One of the early projects of the society was the pooling of medical books and journals. A convenient room was rented and a cooperative library set up, but it lasted only a few years.

The Chester County Medical Society has maintained an active organization from the beginning. At times the interest and attendance have lagged but the organization was always kept intact.

The monthly meeting of the Chester County Medical Society and the staff of the Chester County Hospital, held jointly, are well attended. Guest speakers are frequently invited to contribute to the scientific programs.

CHESTERFIELD COUNTY MEDICAL SOCIETY

The Chesterfield County Medical Society became affiliated with the South Carolina Medical Association by May 1908 with seven members. The officers listed in the 1912 edition of the AMA Directory were Dr. T. E. Lucas, president, and Dr. I. R. Wagner, secretary. The society has remained in active status throughout its history.

CLARENDON COUNTY MEDICAL SOCIETY

The Clarendon County Medical Society became a component society of the South Carolina Medical Association in April 1906 with eight members. The first officers were Dr. H. L. Wilson of Jordan, president, and Dr. L. C. Stukes of Summerville, secretary. It remained in active status until 1938. Apparently the society did not become organized again until it combined with Sumter County's society after World War II.

COLLETON COUNTY MEDICAL SOCIETY

In 1852 the Colleton District Medical Association made an application for a charter to the South Carolina Medical Association and became a component society with 20 members. Dr. Thomas Lining was its first president. Nothing more is known of its activity until the society was reorganized by Dr. Charles S. Esdorn in 1905. It became affiliated with the SCMA by September 1905, meeting monthly, with five members and Dr. Esdorn as its secretary. Although no records are available from the society itself, it has reported officers to the American Medical Association until the present. In recent years it has met with the medical staff of the Colleton County Hospital; officers and members the same for both organizations.

COLUMBIA MEDICAL SOCIETY OF RICHLAND COUNTY

The members of this society, organized March 13, 1854, went through the vicissitudes of the Civil War and the period of stagnation thereafter with activity of variable intensity. The society was reorganized in 1865 and again in 1904 as the Richland County Medical Society, when it became a component part of the South Carolina Medical Association. In the year previous the society had adopted a new constitution and fee bill and expressed its vital interest in matters of sanitation and proper water supply for the city. It proposed to the municipal authorities the erection of a hospital for Negro patients but its proposal was received with "frosty frigidity" and nothing was accomplished.

In 1926 the society had 86 members. It interested itself in the general sanitary problems of the city and in the improvement of the water supply. It also concerned itself further with the plan to establish a hospital for Negroes. In 1937, at the instigation of Dr. William Weston, broad plans for programs with outstanding speakers were established. The society bulletin *The Recorder,* was also started at that time. The society's growing library was moved to the Columbia Hospital.

In 1938 the society was incorporated as the Columbia Medical Society of Richland County, a name not to be confused with that of the short-lived Richland County Medical Society which was organized and incorporated by a disgruntled member of the older society, but had a very brief existence and boasted only two members.

In 1942 there were 44 members of the Columbia Medical Society in the medical corps of the armed services. The society has continued to grow rapidly and is now the largest in South Carolina. It maintains its excellent programs with well known speakers and participates in all the aspects of medicine in the state.

DARLINGTON COUNTY MEDICAL SOCIETY

In 1885 the Darlington County Medical Association had 22 members and set up a Fee Bill for post-mortem examinations. How long this organization was active is not known, possibly from 1875 to 1890. It was reorganized under the name of the Darlington County Medical Society in 1904 and became a component society of the SCMA by August 1906 with 14 members. It has continued on a fairly active status since this time except for the period of World War II when it ceased temporarily to hold meetings.

A photograph of the Darlington County Medical Association of 1885 is extant.

DILLON COUNTY MEDICAL SOCIETY

In 1910 Dillon County was formed from Marion County. The first listing of the Dillon County Medical Society as a component society of the SCMA is in the AMA Directory of 1912, with Dr. T. H. Smith as president and Dr. D. M. Michaux as secretary. A fee bill was issued in 1914 by five doctors of Dillon County Officers of the society were reported in all of the AMA directories until the late 1950's. It continues as an active society.

DORCHESTER COUNTY MEDICAL SOCIETY

An application for a charter was granted to the Dorchester County Medical Society in 1902. The society became affiliated with the South Carolina Medical Association by September 1905, with 10 members. It continued to report officers to the AMA until World War II. It was revived briefly in the 1950's but is now no longer functioning.

The Summerville Medical Society published a Fee Bill in 1964, signed by seven members.

EDGEFIELD COUNTY MEDICAL SOCIETY

The Edgefield District Medical Association, organized January 10, 1849 with Dr. J. C. Ready as its president, was the first medical society in the area. When activity in formation of county medical societies increased, a charter was issued by the South Carolina Medical Association to the Edgefield County Medical Society in 1872. Actually the first meeting of this society had been held in the year previous with Dr. W. D. Jennings as president and Dr. W. H. Timmerman as treasurer. The society was reorganized with nine members in 1906 and appears to have functioned until 1926, when it became a part of the Ridge Medical Society.

EDISTO MEDICAL SOCIETY

This society comprises the counties of Bamberg, Calhoun, and Orangeburg. The story of its origin and progress has been lost somewhere along the way. It is listed in the 1934 AMA Directory with Dr. A .W. Browning, president, and Dr. V. W. Brabham, secretary. The Orangeburg and Bamberg medical societies were organized and affiliated with the South Carolina Medical Association in 1906 as separate units and the Calhoun County Medical Society also functioned separately for a time. The Edisto Society has always been a rather loosely organized body and at the present day has no formal constitution, bylaws, or regularly kept minutes.

FAIRFIELD COUNTY MEDICAL SOCIETY

This society was chartered originally by the South Carolina Medical Association in 1889. It continued more or less activity until 1906, when it was reorganized under the general program of improvement of county societies. In 1906 it had seven members.

In the decades of the 1920's and 1930's the physicians of Fairfield were closely associated with the Fifth District Medical Society and the activity of the local society was minimal. In the 1940's they instituted monthly meetings which were held at residences of the members. For the past ten years the meetings have been held at the Fairfield Country Club with the doctors rotating as hosts. The meetings are informal and primarily social. Scientific activities are carried out at staff meetings of the local hospital in Winnsboro. In 1970 Dr. C. S. McCants is president and Dr. Allen P. Jeter is secretary of this organization with a total present membership of six.

FLORENCE COUNTY MEDICAL SOCIETY

At a meeting of the South Carolina Medical Association in 1892 it was reported that the Florence County Medical Society had nine members and had been chartered in March 1892. It became affiliated with the SCMA by October 1905 with six members. It has reported officers to the AMA throughout the years and was incorporated about 15 years ago. It is independent of the Pee Dee Medical Association.

GEORGETOWN COUNTY MEDICAL SOCIETY

The Medical Society of Georgetown District was active in 1848 and possibly earlier. The Georgetown County Medical Society was chartered in February 1892 with nine members. In 1903 it surrendered its charter because its delegates were not seated at the SCMA convention in 1902. However, it became a component society of the state organization by March 1906 with ten members, meeting monthly. Although it continued to report officers to the AMA through the 1920's and 1930's, it appears to have been rather inactive. The society was revived after World War II and was chartered again March 31, 1949 with nine members and Dr. F. A. Bell as president. The present membership is 15.

GREENVILLE COUNTY MEDICAL SOCIETY

By J. DECHERD GUESS, M.D.

The Greenville County Medical Society was the last of what might be called the pioneer societies of the Medical Association. Greenville District, as the area was called until 1868, did not become a part of the state, nor was it opened for settlement, until it was ceded to the state by the Cherokees in 1784.

There were only seven doctors in the county in 1836, a half-century later. Greenville County was not represented at the meeting called in 1848 for the purpose of organizing a state association.

Delegates from Greenville were registered at the state meeting in 1873 for the first time. At that time there were 51 doctors practicing in Greenville County.

In 1879, the society established a reading room and library. However, shortly thereafter, and for what reason is not clear, the society seems to have become inactive. It was revived in 1887 and chartered in 1891 as a constituent society of the South Carolina Medical Association under the name of the Greenville County Medical Association, and held quarterly meetings. In 1888 it had only 12 members.

In 1905, the year following its reorganization, the state Association met in Greenville. A banquet was held, with 250 covers set. The mayor and other dignitaries made speeches, and several Greenville doctors were on the scientific program. Dr. Davis Furman, one of Greenville's most prominent doctors, was elected president of the state Association. It was that meeting, with its excellent scientific program, its banquet, and the election of a Greenville doctor to president, that marked the statewide recognition of the Greenville medical group as an important force in South Carolina medicine.

In 1914, there came a revival of interest. A room in City Hall was secured and a library opened there. This was later combined with the staff library of the Greenville General Hospital. This joint library has been enlarged by regular and systematic purchases of new books and periodicals and later a professional librarian was put in charge.

A new administration with Dr. Thomas Brockman, president, took office in January of 1938. It was suggested that the society establish a society bulletin, the primary purpose of which would be to keep up sustained interest of the members in war service in the affairs of the society and to serve as a medium of communication between the local group and the doctors of the state and those living in contiguous areas of neighboring states. The result was a very successful *Bulletin of the Greenville County Medical Society*. Coincidental with the establishment of *The Bulletin*, the character of the monthly scientific programs was modernized. Since that time invited lecturers of professorial caliber have been asked to speak to the society at each meeting. Fellowship and attendance have been maintained by means of a banquet-type dinner.

The Greenville County Medical Society sent 45 medical officers to the armed forces during World War II. During these war years, physicians were acutely scarce, all were overworked, chronic fatigue was widespread, and although medical care was reasonably satisfactory, it was not up to previous standards, nor was it given with the zest and usual facility. However, it was during these years of overwork and stress that several significant and progressive steps were taken by the society.

In 1945 a foundation for scientific, educational, and charitable purposes was set up as another phase of progressive society activity. Several rather large contributions and many small ones were made to the foundation through the years. When it was established, a building to house the society and its meetings, the establishment and maintenance of a library, and a lounging and dining room were in the planning. After the initial enthusiasm wore off, and after library, reading rooms, and a lounge were included in new hospital construction, interest in the plans faded. At the last report in February 1969, there was $28,250 in the foundation treasury. Its chief use has been to serve as a loan fund to several members who needed funds for advanced professional study.

In 1951, the first training course for practical nurses in South Carolina was promoted by the county society. This initial course given in the Greenville High School has been continued and other similar courses have been established. These courses have aided materially in alleviating the shortage of nursing personnel.

The Greenville County Medical Society in 1969 had a membership of 252 active members and 51 honorary members. Since its charter was granted in 1891, it has been rated as one of the most active and progressive societies in the state. During the three-quarters of a century of its corporate life it has furnished eleven presidents to the Association, several delegates to the American Medical Association, leadership and direction in establishing and maintaining the South Carolina Blue Cross and Blue Shield organizations, sponsorship and direction in setting up and carrying through poliomyelitis and other countywide immunization programs, and has provided the professional personnel of a highly organized and well trained staff for an inclusive county hospital system.

REFERENCES

The Bulletin of the Greenville County Medical Society, Vols. 1-21, 1938-1958.

J. Decherd Guess, M.D., *A Medical History of Greenville County, South Carolina* (Greenville: Published by the Greenville County Medical Society 1959).

J. Decherd Guess, M.D., "The Greenville County Medical Society Historical Sketches," *J. S. Carolina Med. Ass.*, 57:17 (January 1961).

Joseph I. Waring, M.D., *A History of Medicine in South Carolina 1825-1900* (Columbia: Published by the South Carolina Medical Association 1967).

GREENWOOD COUNTY MEDICAL SOCIETY

The Greenwood County Medical Society was organized in 1902, and became a component society of the South Carolina Medical Association by September 1905 with ten members, meeting monthly. Although officers of the society have been reported to the SCMA throughout the years, no record of its early activities is available.

The Greenwood County Medical Society now meets twice a year, in the spring and in the fall. Dr. William Roche is the current president.

HAMPTON COUNTY MEDICAL SOCIETY

The Hampton County Medical Society became a component society of the South Carolina Medical Association by September 1905 with nine members. It fell into inactivity but was reorganized in 1916. Again it was dissolved until the 1930's, when it became part of the Savannah Valley Medical Society with Allendale and Barnwell counties. This joint society went out of existence about the time of World War II. A listing as the Hampton County Medical Society reappeared in the AMA Directory of 1956, and the society continues as a member of the Association.

HORRY COUNTY MEDICAL SOCIETY

The Horry County Medical Society was organized in 1905 and became a component society of the South Carolina Medical Association by January 1906 with six members, meeting monthly. Its first officers were Dr. H. H. Burroughs, president, and Dr. J. A. Norton, secretary. Although nothing is known of its activities, it reported officers to the AMA up until World War II when it became disorganized.

The Horry County Medical Society now has a membership of 46 and has been holding regular meetings since 1949. The president is Dr. W. S. A. Harris of Myrtle Beach.

JASPER COUNTY MEDICAL SOCIETY

Jasper became a county of the state in 1912. The first time the Jasper County Society is listed in the AMA Directories is in 1929 when it was combined with Beaufort County to form a joint society. The Beaufort-Jasper Society continued to report officers except for the period of World War II, until the late 1950's or early 1960's when the society became known again as the Beaufort County Medical Society. Many of the physicians in Jasper County participate in Coastal Medical Society activities.

KERSHAW COUNTY MEDICAL SOCIETY

The Camden Medical Society was in existence in 1819, when it published a fee bill. The Medical Association of Kershaw District was organized in 1866. In 1874 it was still active with Dr. E. M. Boykin, president, and Dr. A. A. Moore, secretary. The Kershaw County Medical Society was reorganized in 1904 and received its charter April 12, 1905, with Dr. W. J. Burdell, president, Dr. A. W. Burnett, vice-president, Dr. S. C. Zemp, secretary-treasurer, and nine other members. It has remained an active society throughout its history.

LANCASTER COUNTY MEDICAL SOCIETY

The town of Lancaster had eight physicians in 1900. An historical sketch of the period speaks of them in terms which might well be preserved; "There were eight skillful, experienced, and highly polished physicians, fully up to date and ready to rise at the hour of midnight, all residing in Lancaster or within easy call, and punctual in visiting their patients." These exemplary physicians were Drs. M. P. Crawford, W. M. Crawford, J. Frank Mackey, T. J. Strait, W. J. White, J. E. Poore, G. W. Poovey, and J. D. Funderburk.

The Lancaster County Medical Society is listed in the AMA Directory of 1916 with Dr. J. D. Funderburk as president. Apparently it became disorganized, as it was dropped from the listing of county societies in later directories. In 1927 it is listed again with Dr. G. W. Poovey, president, and Dr. R. L. Crawford, Jr., secretary. From that time on it continued to report officers to the AMA. However, no records of the society itself are available before 1940, when the society met with the staff of the Marion Sims Memorial Hospital. There were 11 members in 1940. The activities of the society have continued to the present.

LAURENS COUNTY MEDICAL SOCIETY

A Medical Society of Laurens was active in 1890 with Dr. W. H. Dial as secretary. Possibly it remained active until it became affiliated with the South Carolina Medical Association in 1906 with 21 members and Dr. J. H. Miller, president, and Dr. R. E. Hughes, secretary.

The earliest records of the society itself are from 1911 when there were 34 licensed physicians in the county. For several years the society met four times yearly with the Third District Medical Society in Greenwood, a society which is no longer functioning.

The present membership of the Laurens County Medical Society is 18.

LEE COUNTY MEDICAL SOCIETY

The Lee County Medical Society was organized in 1905 and became affiliated with the South Carolina Medical Association by September 1905, meeting monthly and listing 12 members. Dr. J. R. Bullock of Lucknow was president and Dr. L. H. Jennings of Bishopville was secretary. Although the society continued to report its officers, it was inactive until 1937 or 1938 when Dr. E. A. Hines of Seneca came to Bishopville and reorganized the society with a membership of 10 or 12. It held regular meetings and was quite active for about 15 years after that. In 1952 it became inactive again and has not been revived.

LEXINGTON COUNTY MEDICAL SOCIETY

The Lexington County Medical Society was formed about 1883, under the direction of Dr. D. M. Crosson of Leesville, with 12 members. Dr. J. W. Geiger was the first president and Dr. Crosson the first secretary-treasurer.

In 1885 the society applied for and received a charter from the South Carolina Medical Association. In 1906 it had 15 members.

In 1926, the Lexington County Medical Society joined the Saluda and Edgefield county societies to form a tri-county society named the Ridge Medical Society.

McCORMICK COUNTY

There appears to be no record of any medical organization in McCormick County.

MARION COUNTY MEDICAL SOCIETY

At a meeting of the South Carolina Medical Association in Sumter in 1893 it was reported that a Marion County Medical Society was "in existence". It became affiliated with the SCMA by September 1905 with 13 members. At that time Dr. Z. G. Smith was president and Dr. H. A. Edwards was secretary. It has continued in an active status throughout the years.

MARLBORO COUNTY MEDICAL SOCIETY

The first records available indicating the existence of the Marlboro County Medical Society date back to 1904, when the constitution and bylaws were printed by the press of the American Medical Association. However, the society was evidently formed some years before this, because Dr. J. L. Napier of Marlboro County was presented as a member of the society in the election for the presidency of the South Carolina Medical Association in 1896. In 1906 the society had 17 members.

Very little is known about its activities until 1920 when four of its members, C. R. May, Thomas H. Smith, J. G. Kinney, and Douglas Jennings made plans for conducting a meeting to be known as the Annual New Year's Meeting to be held in January of each year. The purpose of this meeting was to afford the physicians from the bordering counties of the two Carolinas the opportunity of meeting together for a dinner and to discuss current scientific matters. The first of these meetings, held in 1920 in the home of one of the members, was attended by approximately 12 doctors. This proved to be a gay evening and everyone departed in his Model T determined to be present the following January. Over a period of years this gathering grew too large for a home and was moved to the Masonic Hall and Legion Hut, and later to the Country Club. More and more physicians began attending from the two Carolinas and Virginia and the main speaker was selected from the larger cities and medical schools. Excepting the papers, the only constant features have been oyster pie and bourbon whiskey.

The Marlboro County Medical Society has had three of its members elected to the presidency of the South Carolina Medical Association—J. L. Napier in 1896, C. R. May, Sr. in 1930, and Douglas Jennings, Sr. in 1940. The Tri-State Medical Association was also served by Dr. Jennings as president, and Dr. May as vice-president.

The year 1960 marked the thirty-ninth Annual New Year's Meeting and a large number of old friends attended. Several of the guests had attended every meeting. The society in 1960 was composed of 12 active members who felt a certain amount of pride in the fact that this annual meeting attracted 135 to 150 physicians from several states.

This meeting continues to be active and popular.

NEWBERRY COUNTY MEDICAL SOCIETY

Although this society sent delegates to the South Carolina Medical Association convention in 1873, very little is known about it until it reorganized and became affiliated with the SCMA by March 1906 with 15 members. Dr. J. M. Kibler of Newberry was president and Dr. J. J. Dominick of Prosperity was secretary. It has continued in its function as a component society.

OCONEE COUNTY MEDICAL SOCIETY

The Oconee County Medical Society applied for and received a charter from the South Carolina Medical Association in 1874. Apparently it became inactive, as the records of the society show an organizational meeting in Walhalla in 1903 with 19 charter members. In 1906 there were 14 members. In 1907 a fee bill was issued and published in the *Journal of the South Carolina Medical Association*. A notable service was rendered to this society by Dr. E. A. Hines, who served as secretary for over 30 years.

Pickens and Oconee societies formerly had joint meetings once a year but this arrangement has been discontinued.

ORANGEBURG COUNTY MEDICAL SOCIETY

First a district society in the middle of the 19th century, the Orangeburg County Medical Society became a component society of the South Carolina Medical Association by June 1906 with 22 members, meeting monthly. Dr. W. L. Pou of St. Matthews was president and Dr. L. C. Shecut of Orangeburg was secretary. By 1914 Orangeburg and Calhoun counties had joined together to form a society but this combination was short-lived, and the two counties became separate societies. During the 1930's Orangeburg, Calhoun, and Bamberg counties joined together to form the Edisto Medical Society, which has continued to the present.

PICKENS COUNTY MEDICAL SOCIETY

The Pickens County Medical Society was organized in 1890 and became a component society of the South Carolina Medical Association by September 1905 with 13 members, meeting monthly. A fee bill was published in 1908. It has continued to function in its original relationship.

RIDGE MEDICAL SOCIETY

The Ridge Medical Society, a continuation of the Second District or Ridge Medical Association, in 1926 became a tri-county organization embracing Lexington, Saluda, and Edgefield counties. In 1929 Dr. A. R. Nicholson, Jr. of Edgefield was president and Dr. W. P. Timmerman of Batesburg was secretary.

The society has continued on an active status. At the present time there are 14 members.

Saluda County Medical Society

The Saluda County Medical Society became affiliated with the South Carolina Medical Association by September 1905 with nine members. Dr. J. D. Waters of Coleman was listed as secretary of the society in 1906 and served in this capacity for over 20 years. In the late 1920's Saluda joined with Edgefield and Lexington counties to form the Ridge Medical Society.

Savannah Valley Medical Society

The Savannah Valley Medical Society had a brief existence in the 1930's when Allendale, Barnwell, and Hampton county societies joined together under this name. Dr. W. R. Tuten of Fairfax was president and Dr. J. F. Kneece of Blackville was secretary. World War II apparently contributed to its demise.

Spartanburg County Medical Society

The first organization of the Spartanburg County Society was accomplished as far back as January 1866 when seven physicians formed a unit. There is no record to tell how well this society prospered, though it is likely that it continued in a more or less active form up until the 20th century.

Reorganization was carried out in 1901 with Dr. J. O. Vernon of Wellford as president. Meetings were held once a month at the old Y.M.C.A. building on Magnolia Street. The subjects of discussion were usually those which were of greatest current local pertinence, *i.e.,* typhoid fever, tuberculosis, and scarlet fever.

After some years the meeting place was changed to a building on West Main Street, which had been a livery stable, and later the Franklin Hotel ballroom was used.

The members of the county medical society were most cooperative in lending assistance to the investigation into the causes of pellagra which took place in Spartanburg in 1914 and later. For the past half century the Spartanburg society has continued its activities, and a number of its members have played prominent parts in the South Carolina Medical Association.

Sumter County Medical Society

The Sumter County Medical Society was organized in 1873 with Dr. J. B. Witherspoon, president. It held quarterly meetings with 17 members. How long it remained active is not known. However, in 1891 the Sumter County Medical Association adopted a constitution and fee bill and was chartered by the South Carolina Medical Association in August of that year. Dr. S. C. Baker was secretary.

In the general reorganization of county societies conducted by the SCMA and the AMA in the early 1900's Sumter County Medical Society became affiliated with the state organization by September 1905, with 11 members meeting monthly. It has been an active society throughout the years. After World War II the doctors of Clarendon County were included in this society.

UNION COUNTY MEDICAL SOCIETY

The Union County Medical Society was organized in 1903 and became affiliated with the South Carolina Medical Association by September 1905 with 15 members. Its first officers were Drs. J. M. Lawson, president; C. Torrence, vice-president; W. G. Fike, second vice-president; and Theodore Maddox, secretary-treasurer.

It has remained an active society throughout the 20th century. The present membership is 8.

WILLIAMSBURG COUNTY MEDICAL SOCIETY

The Williamsburg County Medical Society was organized and became affiliated with the South Carolina Medical Association by March 1906, with four members meeting monthly. Dr. J. D. Whitehead of Lake City was president and Dr. L. B. Salters of Lake City was secretary. In 1908 the society published a fee bill and "black list". Although the society continued to report officers throughout the years, it was apparently inactive for much of this time. When Dr. Michael Holmes came to Kingstree in 1947 he made a move to reorganize a county medical society with the result that occasional informal medical gatherings were held. The first meeting of the newly reorganized society was February 19, 1955. Meetings have been held at least twice a year and, when the Williamsburg County Memorial Hospital was constructed, it became the place of meeting. Out-of-town speakers are frequently invited. Dr. Vernon L. Bauer of Hemingway was secretary-treasurer for a number of years, later succeeded by Dr. J. C. Montgomery, who was followed by Dr. Michael Holmes.

YORK COUNTY MEDICAL SOCIETY

One of the earliest district medical societies of the Association, the York County Medical Society became a component society of the South Carolina Medical Association by September 1905 with 19 members. Bi-monthly meetings were scheduled. Dr. E. W. Pressly of Clover was president and Dr. J. R. Miller of Rock Hill was secretary. For a time it was affiliated with the Fifth District Medical Society.

The present membership is 43. The society meets monthly except during the summer. The December meeting is Ladies Night, a meeting held jointly with the York County Medical Auxiliary.

CHAPTER 6

THE DISTRICT MEDICAL SOCIETIES

The first permanent medical organization in South Carolina was the Medical Society of South Carolina, founded in 1789, intended as a statewide group but actually representing the Charleston area. When this society in 1848 invited the physicians of the state to establish the South Carolina Medical Association, it requested that representatives from the various districts meet to organize. Sixteen of the 29 judicial districts of the state were represented. Councillors for the participating districts were elected by the Medical Association at the time of its organization. They constituted a board composed of one representative for each five fellows of the Association in each district and were supposed to meet three times a year. The districts were abolished in 1868 and replaced by 31 counties.

Charters were issued to the various district societies by the state Medical Association. In 1850, 17 districts were represented at the annual meeting, but only five district societies were active. After the reorganization of the Association following the Civil War there was a movement to form county societies, but apparently this effort did not succeed to any degree until 1891, when these societies were encouraged actively by the state Association. In 1905 a major revival of interest in county societies was accomplished with the aid of a representative from the American Medical Association.

Information on the district societies is scanty. Already the recollection of their activities seems to have faded largely out of mind. Such facts as could be gathered are listed below.

Charleston District was organized in 1848 and continued for some time as a locally inclusive society. Colleton District was established in 1849 and Beaufort followed in the same year. Over the years various additions and changes were made in the affiliations of the several counties.

In 1915 the First District was organized. It now includes five counties of the area adjacent to Charleston County, to make a county membership of six.

The Second District (Ridge) Medical Association was organized in Batesburg, S. C. July 1910 with the following officers; Dr. J. J. Wingard of Lexington, president; Dr. J. J. Cleckley, vice-president;

Dr. Sophia Brunson, secretary and treasurer; Dr. R. H. Timmerman, councillor. The dues of the society were 50 cents a year. The second meeting was held in January 1911 in Bamberg. The third meeting was in St. Matthews July 1911, when Dr. Cleckley was made president; Dr. T. H. Dreher, vice-president; and Dr. Sophia Brunson, secretary and treasurer.

The counties originally included in this district were Bamberg, Orangeburg, Calhoun, and Lexington. In 1912, the districts were changed to place the counties of Lexington, Saluda, Aiken, and Edgefield in the second district with Dr. W. T. Timmerman as councillor. The district society was reorganized in Ridge Spring, whence it acquired its unofficial name. Constitution and bylaws were adopted. Meetings were held twice a year, most often in Lexington County. Programs included two or three local speakers and invited guests. In April 1920 the districts were changed so as to place Edgefield, Saluda, Lexington, Richland, Calhoun, and Orangeburg counties in the second district with Dr. S. E. Harmon as councillor. Dues were increased to two dollars per annum. Rules and regulations presented by Dr. W. P. Timmerman, president of the South Carolina Medical Association were adopted.

The district association went well for a number of years. The tricounty meeting of Lexington, Saluda, and Edgefield counties, inaugurated in 1926, continued active until about 1955 or 1956. With many other nearby medical meetings, courses, and seminars becoming available, interest declined to a vanishing point. No meetings have been held by this group for a number of years.

The Third District was organized in 1910. This society was variably active for a good many years, meeting quarterly for some 12 to 15 years. It had good programs and an annual ladies night dinner. About 1932 it began having only an annual dinner meeting, primarily for the purpose of nominating a councillor. It appears to have ceased to function.

The Fourth District was organized in 1906 and after a career of variable activity, was reorganized in 1919. According to one reliable source (Dr. E. A. Hines) this district was first organized in 1896 and was the first one in the state.

The Fifth District Medical Society was organized "some time before World War I". For many years it was very active. Apparently there has been no meeting since about 1963. Early meetings included an all-day session, morning and evening, with dinner in the middle of the day. Practically no records are available. The organization now seems rather dead.

The Sixth District's date of organization is unknown but was before 1902 or thereabouts. The Pee Dee Medical Association and the Sixth District were more or less synonymous. Both organizations met as the Pee Dee Association but carried on the business of the district medical society. This situation continued until the end of World War II when the Pee Dee Association became entirely separated and Horry County withdrew from the Pee Dee Association. The district society has been almost entirely inactive, meeting only to elect delegates and a councillor for the South Carolina Medical Association.

The Seventh District was organized in 1910, according to Dr. Michael Holmes. When Dr. Holmes came to Kingstree in 1933 there was a district society which met regularly. Most of the meetings were held in Sumter. Dr. Holmes believes that the society had been active for 35 years, since 1932. All the counties in the district except Lee County now have separate societies. Clarendon and Sumter counties have combined to form one society.

The Eighth District Medical Society has for many years been a very loosely organized group without an active program and no slate of officers. For the past fifteen years or more it has met once a year with a dinner meeting and a scientific program. It was organized in 1912.

Bamberg, Calhoun, and Orangeburg counties are now organized loosely in the Edisto Medical Society, which meets regularly.

About 1941 a larger district was divided and a smaller ninth district composed of Spartanburg, Union, and Cherokee counties was created. Dr. Herbert Hames of Jonesville was elected the first president of this new district society. Meetings have been held alternately at Gaffney, Union, and Spartanburg since that time. As interest in the meetings seemed to decline drastically, Cherokee and Union county societies were invited to meet with the Spartanburg County Medical Society two months previous to the annual meeting of the South Carolina Medical Association to conduct the formal business of the district. This meeting was held in conjunction with the regular meeting of the Spartanburg County Medical Society.

After the organization and increased activity of the county societies, the old district societies, while having no real official status in the Association other than to elect councillors to the South Carolina Medical Association, continued with varying degrees of activity. Meetings were held once or twice a year with scientific programs and some transactions of business. The increasing availability of other sources of medical information through seminars, postgraduate courses, etc. caused the district activities to decline. Some of these societies now exist largely for the purpose of selecting councillors for the South Carolina Medical Association and show very little other activity.

The present composition (1971) of the Districts of the South Carolina Medical Association is as follows:

First District—Beaufort, Berkeley, Charleston, Colleton, Dorchester, and Jasper Counties

Second District—Aiken, Edgefield, Lexington, Richland, and Saluda Counties

Third District—Abbeville, Greenwood, Laurens, Newberry, and McCormick Counties

Fourth District—AnJerson, Greenville, Oconee, and Pickens Counties

Fifth District—Chester, Fairfield, Kershaw, Lancaster, and York Counties

Sixth District—Chesterfield, Darlington, Dillon, Florence, Horry, Marion, and Marlboro Counties

Seventh District—Clarendon, Georgetown, Lee, Sumter, and Williamsburg Counties

Eighth District—Allendale, Bamberg, Barnwell, Calhoun, Hampton, and Orangeburg Counties

Ninth District—Cherokee, Spartanburg, and Union Counties

COASTAL MEDICAL SOCIETY

On July 12, 1934, Drs. L. M. Stokes, J. B. Johnston, A. R. Johnston, W. A. Black, Carroll Brown, and several others from the coastal counties met in Walterboro to discuss the organization of a medical society which would include the counties then not actively organized. These were Hampton, Jasper, Beaufort, Colleton, Dorchester, and Berkeley.

It was decided to form a medical society composed of physicians from the coastal area with the name of the Coastal Medical Society. The following officers were elected: Dr. J. B. Johnston, president; Dr. L. M. Stokes, vice-president, and Dr. W. A. Black, secretary. Meetings were held by invitation in the various towns of the participating counties.

As time progressed, the society grew in membership and functioned very nicely until 1944-1945, when it became necessary to discontinue meetings because of the demands of the then current war. Meetings were resumed in September 1945. With the return of the local physicians and others coming into the area, the society developed a good membership and continued to progress. In 1949 it comprised Charleston, Jasper, Beaufort, Hampton, Colleton, and Dorchester counties.

In recent years the society has held its seven scheduled meetings annually and listed a membership of 50, who gave an average attendance of 35.

THE PEE DEE MEDICAL ASSOCIATION

This is one of the oldest associations of the state. It was organized with 13 members in 1848, perhaps before, and was primarily for physicians from the Pee Dee section of South Carolina, *i. e.*, the counties of Marlboro, Marion, Darlington, Chesterfield, and Horry. Later Dillion and Florence, created subsequently to the original group, were added. A constitution, a code of ethics, and a fee bill were properly adopted.

No record remains of the early activities of the association but it is likely that it continued at a rather slow pace for most of its life up to and into the 20th century. In 1910 Dr. F. H. McLeod bent his efforts toward rejuvenation of the rather moribund organization. Speakers from outside the area were obtained frequently. Meetings were held at various towns of the area, although they were usually in Florence.

For a short time the organization was known as the Four County Society, later the Seven County Society, but the original name was resumed. In 1948 the *Bulletin of the Pee Dee Medical Association* was inaugurated with Dr. Joseph Cain of Mullins as editor, and it

was published monthly as a news bulletin and informational literature for the association.

The Pee Dee Medical Association has practically ceased activity,
but plans for revival are under way.

REFERENCE

Julian P. Price, M.D., *Brief Historical Sketch of the Pee Dee Medical
Association Commemorating Its One Hundredth Anniversary 1848-1948*
(Florence, S. C.).

CHAPTER 7

THE SPECIALTY SOCIETIES

CAROLINA UROLOGICAL ASSOCIATION

A society known as the South Carolina Urological Association was organized at Charleston on November 8, 1927 by the joint efforts of Dr. James J. Ravenel of Charleston and Dr. Milton Weinberg of Sumter. Its first annual meeting with 14 members present was held February 7, 1928, at which time the name was changed to the Urological Association of South Carolina. Dr. Weinberg was its first president, Dr. Ravenel its second. It is supposed to have been the first or one of the first of such organizations in the United States.

This group met regularly for many years until some time in the early 1950's, when interest and activity lagged. Dr. Paul Sanders, Jr. was its last president. About 1967 its members combined with the North Carolina Urological Association to form the Carolina Urological Association. Dr. Phillips Bates of Greenwood was president-elect for 1970.

INDUSTRIAL MEDICAL ASSOCIATION

The society was formed in 1954. It grew a little and then fell into atrophy, possibly because there was no school of occupational medicine at the Medical University. It has now merged with the North Carolina society to form the Carolina Industrial Medical Association. It is a component society of the Industrial Medical Association of the United States which publishes the *Journal of Occupational Medicine.*

The association meets twice a year, in the spring and fall. There are now about 60 or 70 members in the Carolina Industrial Medical Association. Membership is not limited to full-time industrial physicians.

THE SOUTH CAROLINA ASSOCIATION OF PUBLIC HEALTH PHYSICIANS

The South Carolina Association of Public Health Physicians was originated on September 8, 1958. Membership is composed of the medical directors in public health activities in South Carolina. This includes the directors in the central office of the State Board of Health, county health officers, and their assistants.

This association is an affiliate of the American Association of Public Health Physicians. It has four meetings a year, including one that occurs at the same time as that of the South Carolina Public Health Association. At this meeting, problems of special concern in the field are discussed. This association is not related to the South Carolina Public Health Association.

SOUTH CAROLINA CHAPTER, AMERICAN COLLEGE OF SURGEONS

In June 1950 this chapter of the American College of Surgeons was organized tentatively with Dr. Weston C. Cook as temporary secretary and Dr. William H. Prioleau as president. Formation of the chapter was assisted by members of the Georgia chapter of the American College of Surgeons. Application for a charter was made in 1951 by the new group. The adoption of a constitution was postponed at the organizational meeting until such time as the American College of Surgeons could form a model version. Original temporary officers were confirmed as permanent occupants of their positions.

When the College of Surgeons' constitution and bylaws were presented, one exception was made by the South Carolina group, namely that all fellows of the American College of Surgeons in South Carolina were eligible provided they were members of the South Carolina Medical Association. Granting of the charter was postponed until 1951 because of this exception which the South Carolina Chapter wished to make.

This chapter was recorded as being the third to become organized and request a charter after the new approved national pattern of bylaws was established. The provision of the South Carolina Chapter was not acceptable to the national body. On November 5, 1952 the chapter voted that memberships be opened to all members of the American College of Surgeons in the state, eliminating the earlier provision.

In 1970 there are approximately 250 members of the South Carolina Chapter and an additional 50 surgeons who are in the candidate group, to be approved upon completion of certain training programs. The chapter meets annually, in recent years in conjunction with the scientific section of the South Carolina Medical Association. It has sponsored one day of the scientific meeting and with the revised program of 1970 will continue to sponsor some part of the presentations.

Officers in 1970 are Drs. Charles B. Hanna, president; Richard Wilson, vice-president, and Bernard E. Ferrara, secretary-treasurer. The chapter operates under a council composed of six men, including the president, secretary-treasurer, and past president. It has a delegate to the national college who is known as the governor and who serves on the board of the American College of Surgeons. Dr. William Cantey is governor at present and has been for a number of years. The chapter makes a cash award and gives a gold medal to a senior student at the Medical University who produces a satisfactory research paper. A similar award is given to a post-graduate student.

THE SOUTH CAROLINA CHAPTER OF THE AMERICAN ACADEMY OF GENERAL PRACTICE

This chapter was organized in 1947 and held its first annual meeting late in 1949. Dr. Henry F. Hall of Columbia was its first president. From a small beginning the chapter had grown to include over 400 members in 1970.

THE SOUTH CAROLINA CHAPTER, AMERICAN ACADEMY OF PEDIATRICS

The South Carolina Chapter of the American Academy of Pediatrics was organized at Columbia September 9, 1952 to include the 16 members of the Academy then active in the state. It has met once a year and elected a state chairman every three years. Annual dues are minimal.

Constitution and bylaws were revised in 1958 and again in 1970. There are now 80 members of the chapter.

THE SOUTH CAROLINA DISTRICT BRANCH OF THE AMERICAN PSYCHIATRIC ASSOCIATION

The advisability of organizing a South Carolina District Branch of the American Psychiatric Association among the 36 association members in South Carolina was presented in 1956 by Dr. William S. Hall.

In March 1957, Dr. Hall communicated with each potential member in South Carolina with full explanation of the policies and procedures of the American Psychiatric Association District Branches, and an invitation to become a charter member of the proposed South Carolina District Branch.

Admission of the District Branch to the Assembly of District Branches was officially approved by the American Psychiatric Association at the annual session on May 15, 1957.

The first independent meeting of the South Carolina District Branch was held in Columbia on March 3, 1960 with Dr. Joe E. Freed of Columbia as the president.

When this District Branch was first organized, it scheduled two meetings each year—a scientific meeting in the fall with an outstanding program and a report of the preceding annual meeting of the Assembly of District Branches, American Psychiatric Association, and a second meeting in the spring for the election of officers and discussion of matters to be presented by the delegate to the Assembly of District Branches at the forthcoming association convention.

The South Carolina District Branch has been officially approved to process applications for membership in the American Psychiatric Association.

Efforts of the branch resulted in legislative creation of a Department of Mental Retardation which replaced the three separate and independent boards previously governing institutions for mental retardates. The branch also participated in the promotion of legislation to license psychologists.

Membership in 1969 stood at 32.

PSYCHIATRY IN SOUTH CAROLINA

In the very earliest stage of the colony of South Carolina, some provision was made for care of the poor and insane. The latter category included slaves with psychiatric problems. Charleston had an alms house which made separate arrangements for some 20 psychiatric patients. The Lunatic Asylum in Columbia began to function in 1828. Dr. James Davis, its first physician, probably should be considered the first specializing psychiatrist in the state. The great advances made in psychiatry in the latter part of the 19th century and in the early 20th century, due to the work of Freud, Adler, and Jung, the development of tests of intelligence, and of the whole field of social psychiatry has changed the picture radically in South Carolina from that of even a fairly recent day.

Among the pioneers in the state was Dr. James W. Babcock, who was the superintendent of the State Hospital for many years (1891-1914), and was particularly interested in pellagra, especially as a cause of dementia. After Dr. Babcock's resignation, Dr. T. J.

Strait served briefly until Dr. C. Frederick Williams succeeded him and remained as superintendent for 30 years. Dr. Williams was a prominent social psychiatrist of his day and a pioneer in malarial fever therapy for general paresis.

Interest in mental health beginning in the early 1920's resulted finally in the establishment of the Department of Mental Health for the state in 1964. In 1895 the Lunatic Asylum had been renamed the State Hospital for the Insane and in 1920 it was named officially the South Carolina State Hospital. Mental hygiene clinics were established at the hospital in 1923 and at various parts of the state with Dr. William P. Beckman for years the deputy director. The 1947 federal act provided funds for mental hygiene services and establishment of permanent clinics in the state.

In 1952 the governing board of the State Hospital was renamed the Mental Health Commission, which assumed the duties of the old organization of Regents.

In the early 1900's pellagra was a major contributor to mental disease in South Carolina. Despite the fact that its dietary origin had been thoroughly suspected for a great many years, and that efforts were being made in the state to reduce this serious problem, its continuing importance as a prevailing disease is evidenced by the occurrence of 637 deaths in 1931. The program of the State Board of Health to supply brewer's yeast to combat the deficiencies of diet causative of pellagra was begun in 1929.

Under Governor James F. Byrnes general interest in the plight of the State Hospital and its patients was developed and the governor was responsible for influencing the legislature to provide considerable appropriations for improving the hospital's physical plants and increasing the scope of its activities. This was the beginning of a state of relative prosperity for the hospital which has continued until the present.

Largely through the efforts of Dr. William S. Hall, in 1957 at a meeting in Columbia the South Carolina District Branch of the American Psychiatric Association was established with 24 members. That the number was doubled in the following year indicates that interest in the specialty was increasing rapidly and that the state was getting a share of psychiatrists. Under a statute of 1964 the South Carolina State Department of Mental Health was given a more precise role and the title of Dr. William S. Hall was changed from Director of Mental Health to that of state Commissioner of Mental Health.

The South Carolina Society for Mental Hygiene, founded November 8, 1927 is still active under the name of the South Carolina Mental Health Association.

The vast extension of the psychiatrist's sphere in the last few decades has been reflected in increased activities in South Carolina. The "open door" policy of hospitals, home visits, clinics, the change from the effort to provide custodial care to furnishing rehabilitation, greater concern with children's problems, and wide expansion of the activities of social workers have all produced a new picture. Time, place, and duration of treatment of patients have changed materially. Hospital stays have been shortened, and the utilization of new drugs has opened a new field of hope and accomplishment.

In past years the picture of the mental hospital population has changed radically. A comparison of relative figures compiled in 1926 with those of 1961 shows that the schizophrenic patients made up in 1961 only a small fraction of their earlier number, and cerebral, arterial, and senile psychoses have doubled in relative frequency. On the other hand, general paresis of the insane has fallen to a very low figure, and pellagra, still important in 1926, has disappeared from the hospital census, although it has not disappeared from the state.*

Certain private institutions of the 20th century were active for many years, such as Waverley Sanitarium in Columbia, founded in 1914 by Dr. and Mrs. James Babcock and for many years an extremely useful resource for the private patient. Waverley performed a needed function in taking some of the load from the State Hospital and served as a place where the acute psychotic could find haven for short periods. The atmosphere was informal and homelike. A memorial wing was added in 1962. Technical hospital standardization and the rise in wages were eventually the causes of the decline of this sanitarium to its closure in 1968. It was then used for the day care of the mentally retarded. Privately operated, it is called the "Babcock Center".

Edgewood Sanitarium was opened by Dr. Orin Yost as a 30-bed private psychiatric institution in Aiken in 1946. In its second year of operation it was enlarged to accommodate 45 patients, and in 1948 because of the increasing demand for services, the plant in Aiken was abandoned and the sanitarium was set up in the old

---

* Information from practitioners of the state indicated that 72 cases of pellagra had been seen in 1968.

World War II Air Force Training Base in Orangeburg, where it soon reached a capacity of 100 beds.

All forms of psychiatric therapy were utilized and yearly psychiatric institutes for physicians and appropriate civic groups were held. In 1951 Dr. R. Ramsey Mellette became the clinical director and shortly after that a geriatric building was added to the plant. Because of Dr. Yost's illness, Dr. Mellette became the medical director and continued in that position until called into active duty in the service in July 1953. Shortly thereafter Dr. Yost decided to give up the sanitarium.

There are now psychiatric units in five general hospitals in addition to the unit at the hospital of the Medical University in Charleston.

Pineland, a state training school and hospital for the mentally retarded, was established by the Department of Mental Health in 1952 and was activated in the following year. Dr. Hall acted as temporary superintendent until Dr. Edward A. Rondeau came into full time office in 1966. With the creation of the South Carolina Mental Retardation Department in 1968, Pineland was set up as a separate institution with its own commission.

THE TEACHING OF PSYCHIATRY IN SOUTH CAROLINA

Prior to the establishment of the department of psychiatry at the Medical College in 1946 there was little teaching of this subject. Members of the staff of the State Hospital came down from Columbia and gave two or three lectures a year to the senior students. These lectures were concerned chiefly with commitment procedures to the State Hospital. Dr. Olin Chamberlain became the first professor of psychiatry in 1946 and Dr. Jennings Cleckley joined the department in 1947 as a part-time faculty member. In 1948 Dr. Joseph H. Marshall became a member of the department. Under Dr. Chamberlain's influence, considerable curriculum time for the teaching of psychiatry was authorized by the faculty, with a series of didactic lectures scheduled during the junior year and a clinical rotation for seniors. Clinical teaching was carried out in the psychiatric unit of the old (1906) Roper Hospital. Facilities there were very limited and the unit was primarily for the housing of patients who could not be left at large or who might be waiting to enter the State Hospital.

In 1952 Dr. Chamberlain retired because of illness and Dr. Cleckley assumed the role of acting chairman of the division until

1956 when the division was separated from the medical department and became an autonomous department. Dr. Cleckley became chairman and remained in that capacity until his resignation in 1968, when he was succeeded by Dr. R. Layton McCurdy.

In 1954 a three year residency program approved by the American Board of Psychiatry and Neurology was the first such program in the state. In 1956 a psychiatric floor was activated in the Medical College Hospital and included 22 beds, later expanded to 66, along with additional office space, therapy departments, etc.

The department has continued to grow with a large increase in the number of full time faculty members and the extension of curriculum time to about three times its original size.

(Much information on matters pertaining to psychiatry has been obtained through the kindness of Mrs. Inez Nolan Fripp, historian, South Carolina Department of Mental Health.)

THE SOUTH CAROLINA OBSTETRICAL AND GYNECOLOGICAL SOCIETY

The South Carolina Obstetrical and Gynecological Society was founded in 1946 at an organizational meeting held in Charleston. Dr. L. A. Wilson was the instigating force in the founding of the society and was elected as the first president. Dr. Manly Hutchinson of Columbia was the vice-president, and Dr. Decherd Guess was the secretary-treasurer. The first meeting was held in Columbia on July 6, 1947 at the Columbia Hotel and the second meeting in 1948 was in Camden.

The society was founded for the purpose of promoting fellowship among its members, to stimulate educational advancement, and to encourage better obstetrical and gynecological practice within the state to the end that South Carolina women should receive more efficient diagnostic and therapeutic care and that mortality and morbidity should be reduced. These tenets have continued to prevail since the society's founding.

In 1970 the society had just over 100 members.

THE SOUTH CAROLINA PEDIATRIC SOCIETY

At a meeting of the South Carolina Medical Association in 1921, seven physicians interested in pediatrics organized the South Carolina Pediatric Society. To this nucleus additional charter members were added to make a total of 12. Dr. W. P. Cornell, then of Columbia, was elected president and Dr. R. M. Pollitzer was given the task of writing the constitution.

Regular and associate members were provided for. In 1922 all physicians interested in pediatrics were invited to join and the membership rose to 39. The size of the society has varied and sometimes it has carried on with only a few faithful members. Now its activities seem firm both scientifically and socially.

Meetings are held annually, with a dinner and presentation of papers.

THE SOUTH CAROLINA RADIOLOGICAL SOCIETY

The South Carolina Radiological Society was organized on June 9, 1932 in Columbia. Dr. Floyd Rogers acted as preliminary chairman and was subsequently elected president. Dr. Robert B. Taft of Charleston was the first secretary. There were 8 charter members: Dr. Percy Hay of Florence, Dr. William Sheridan of Greenville, Dr. D. Baxter of Sumter, Dr. Hillyer Rudisill of Charleston, Dr. W. S. Judy of Greenville, Dr. T. A. Pitts of Columbia, Dr. F. Ryon of Anderson, and Dr. Malcolm Mosteller of Columbia.

The society was initially named "The South Carolina X-Ray Society" and the constitution and bylaws were modeled on those of the Florida Roentgen Ray Society, with minor changes, and in 1939 were amended to restrict active membership to diplomates of the American Board of Radiology.

Customarily the society has met twice a year; in the spring in conjunction with the South Carolina Medical Association meeting, and in the fall, at the discretion of the president and the program chairman.

The society continued to be active during World War II, but the minutes from 1941 through 1949 have been mislaid. In May of 1952, the name was changed to the South Carolina Radiological Society, operating under the original constitution.

The model constitution and bylaws proposed by the American College of Radiology were adopted in 1963, and the society petitioned for admission to the newly organized College system for trial chapter status. On February 2, 1966, the society was chartered in the College as a permanent chapter.

Currently there are 59 members—53 active and 6 associate. Eligibility for membership as an associate is predicated upon completion of an acceptable residency in radiology and board eligibility, licensure in South Carolina, membership in a local medical society, and the full-time practice of radiology. Individuals meeting these requirements and certified by the American Board of Radiology qualify for active membership, which carries the right to vote and hold office. The bylaws also provide for retired and honorary memberships and memberships in physics.

Ten members have been elected as fellows in the American College of Radiology and duly invested. This is considered as an honor bestowed upon individual radiologists in recognition of outstanding achievements and contributions to the specialty and to organized medicine as well as longevity in practice, as indicated by the fact that there are approximately 1,200 fellows in the total membership of just under 7,000 members in the American College of Radiology

NOTE: The x-ray machine apparently was used first in South Carolina by Mr. Charles Colcock of the Porter Military Academy who helped locate a bullet on April 2, 1897. Dr. William Henry Johnson of Charleston used the x-ray "very early," but dates cannot be documented, nor can the statement that Columbia's "Dr. R. W. Gibbes brought the first x-ray machine to South Carolina".*

THE SOUTH CAROLINA SOCIETY OF OPHTHALMOLOGY
AND OTOLARYNGOLOGY

By RODERICK MACDONALD, M.D.

The South Carolina Society of Ophthalmology and Otolaryngology was organized in the early 1920's. At that time the membership was open to all physicians of good standing who were interested in the two specialties. Membership is now limited to physicians who confine their work entirely to these fields. The society has been instrumental in bringing to this state some of the outstanding men of the specialty in America as guest speakers.

For the past 20 years the society has met jointly with the North Carolina Ophthalmology and Otolaryngology Society, alternating between the two states. Meetings are both social and scientific.

This society was the first of its kind to hold a meeting in conjunction with the Founders' Day program formerly held in Charleston each year.

The officers of our state society are for 1970: president, Dr. Lyndell W. Blackman; vice-president, Dr. W. L. Davis; secretary and treasurer, Dr. Clay W. Evatt, Jr. There are 70 members in the society.

---

* *The Recorder* (Columbia Medical Society) 15:9 (September 1951).

THE SOUTH CAROLINA SOCIETY OF PATHOLOGISTS

The initial meeting for organizing this society was held in 1951 in conjunction with the annual meeting of the South Carolina Medical Association. The first officers elected were Drs. H. H. Plowden, president; J. W. MacMeans, vice-president, and E. A. Dreskin, secretary and treasurer. The second meeting was held in July to formulate a constitution and bylaws and the third meeting was held at Anderson during the Piedmont Postgraduate Clinical Assembly. At this last meeting a constitution was adopted and the society was officially established.

In 1953 the membership consisted of 11 physicians. Dr. H. R. Pratt-Thomas served as president from 1953-1958. Dr. Dreskin replaced him and served until 1963. In 1958 there were 16 members of the society, 9 of them from outside of Charleston.

The society has continued active interest in economic and scientific aspects of the practice of pathology and has expressed concern over advertising by commercial laboratories, the establishment of a licensing law for laboratories, and promotion of a state-wide medical examiner system for South Carolina.

In 1970 there are 50 pathologists included in the membership. Clinical meetings are held twice a year. Dr. Donald G. Kilgore, Jr. is president for 1969-1970.

THE SOUTH CAROLINA SURGICAL SOCIETY

This society was organized by Dr. George H. Bunch and Dr. William C. Cantey, both of Columbia. An organizational meeting was held in the spring of 1949. Dr. Bunch was elected president and Dr. Cantey secretary-treasurer. These were both temporary positions.

The first official meeting was held June 23, 1949 in Charleston. Dr. Bunch was confirmed as president, Dr. Roger G. Doughty of Columbia was elected vice-president, and Dr. Cantey as secretary-treasurer. There were 20 charter members of the society.

Subsequent meetings were held chiefly in Columbia but also elsewhere. Membership had risen in 1970 to 119, just below the limited number of 125. Members must be certified by the American Board of Surgery or the American Board of Thoracic Surgery, must pursue a practice limited to surgery or a surgical specialty, and must be recommended by a member of the society.

The South Carolina Thoracic Society

The South Carolina Thoracic Society (formerly the Trudeau Society) is the medical section of the South Carolina Tuberculosis and Respiratory Disease Association and an affiliate of the American Thoracic Society, medical section of the National Tuberculosis and Respiratory Disease Association. The local society was organized in 1946 as an enlargement of the state association's Medical Advisory Committee. Work of this committee had been directed primarily to guidance in the development of case-finding programs of the association and organized efforts to obtain treatment facilities for tuberculosis.

Dr. John F. Busch, who was employed by the South Carolina association in 1944 to direct a tuberculosis "Case Finding Demonstration", recognized medical education as a major factor in a successful tuberculosis program. Dr. Busch arranged for a scientific session to be held in conjunction with the annual meeting of the association. The 1944-1945 association annual report states "with the purpose, primarily of interesting physicians in the clinical aspects of tuberculosis, and, of forming a South Carolina Trudeau Society.

"Upon the passing of a motion made by 26 physicians attending this medical session, steps have been taken to form a South Carolina Trudeau Society".

The 1949-1950 annual report mentions revision of its constitution by the society to read: "The chief purpose of this society is to concentrate its influence and efforts toward the eradication of tuberculosis in cooperation with all medical and lay groups interested in scientific investigation, clinical practice, education, rehabilitation, and public control of the disease.

"The programs shall be chiefly scientific, chiefly presented by members, and supplemented once a year by a speaker to be nominated by the officers and chosen by the members".

Annual scientific programs have been presented each year in conjunction with the annual meeting of the South Carolina Association (SCTRDA).

The society has promoted participation in out-of-state postgraduate courses. In 1955 it joined the Florida and Georgia societies in organizing a Consecutive Case Conference (Pembine type). Dr. John F. Busch with the Veterans Administration in Atlanta was chairman of the steering committee of the 1955 and 1956 conferences. Programs of these conferences are directed to improvement of tuberculosis eradication programs and the major focus has been on treatment of tuberculosis. Dr. E. Y. Smith, Jr., Charleston, was elected chairman for the 1957 conference and since that time the chairman is from South Carolina every third year. Dr. John Preston, Dr. Edmund R. Taylor, and Dr. David B. Gregg have served as chairmen.

The Thoracic Society promoted the adoption of a plan to finance the program of undergraduate medical education in respiratory diseases initiated at the Medical College of South Carolina in 1966. Society members plan and promote postgraduate medical education programs.

There are some 85 or 90 members of the society.

CHAPTER 8

MEDICAL CLUBS, HISTORICAL AND CLINICAL

The Robert Wilson Medical History Club of Charleston

The Medical History Club of Charleston was organized November 5, 1925 at the residence of Dr. Robert Wilson, who was the moving spirit in the undertaking. Dr. Wilson recalled the earlier days of the club thus: "The club was organized by me in the hope through its medium to stimulate interest, especially among the younger men of the profession, in the cultural side of medicine. . . . The first meeting was held at my house and at a second meeting a few days later, I read the first paper on the subject of 'Primitive Medicine'. . . . At the first meeting I served crackers and cheese with certain liquid refreshment. As you know this has been elaborated upon considerably in later years. . . . The absence of the minutes of the first few years makes it impossible to fill in the gaps, but I do not think anything of importance occurred except the reading of the papers. . . ."

The club has had no formal constitution or routine. The only officer has been the secretary, who is elected to serve as long as his behavior is considered satisfactory by the members. (There have been only two.) There are no dues; the secretary asks occasionally for voluntary contributions for minor expenses. The original eight meetings of the year are now reduced to five, and are held by invitation at the homes of the members without any regular rotation. An early understanding that the refreshments (other than liquid) served at these meetings were to be "cheese and crackers" has been honored largely in the breach, but the club has no formal dinners.

Membership is contingent only upon evinced interest in the subject of medical history. If a member fails to appear at meetings, after a reasonable time his name is dropped from the mailing list at the discretion of the secretary—thus the list of members has been very variable.

The first secretary was Dr. W. F. R. Phillips, then professor of anatomy at the Medical College. The older members recall Dr. Phillips' interesting announcement cards for the meetings, and the humorous quality of the minutes. In 1933 Dr. Phillips left Charleston taking with him all the minutes of the meetings up to October of that year, contending that he was the "permanent" secretary of the club and that the minutes were his personal property; he never consented to relinquishing them, and they have disappeared. Consequently, the record of the first eight years of the club's existence is missing.

The club has been a constituent member of the American Association for the History of Medicine since 1939. Its members have contributed a number of articles to the *Journal of the South Carolina Medical Association*, the *Bulletin of the History of Medicine*, to the now inactive *Annals of Medical History* and to other publications.

The club was responsible for introducing a motion in the Medical Society of South Carolina which eventually resulted directly in the creation of the Committee on Historical Medicine of the South Carolina Medical Association in 1937.

In 1929 the club erected a tablet to Dr. Eugene L. Jagar which was placed in the Roper Hospital Clinic and is now in the Medical University Clinic.

In 1936 the club, largely through the efforts of Dr. Hillyer Rudisill, sponsored a museum of roentgenology at the Medical College which unfortunately has been dispersed.

In 1949 the club made a serious effort to stimulate interest in historical lectures at the Medical College. A series of ten annual lectures was scheduled for presentation by different members of the club. The course was not compulsory, and after the first year of effort the plan was abandoned because of lack of interest among the students.

In 1951 the name of the club was changed to the Robert Wilson Medical History Club. In March 1960 the club was the host for the annual meeting of the American Association for the History of Medicine. This was a very successful meeting with good attendance.

The club continues to pursue its usual course with a variety of speakers and papers and entertainment at the homes of the members. Membership ranges from 20 to 25 active members.

THE COLUMBIA MEDICAL CLUB

The Columbia Medical Club was organized in 1923 by some 15 members of the local profession, and was intended as an informal forum for the discussion of cultural and historical matters related to medicine. Members were chosen from the several specialties in medicine and the original intention was to increase the total membership to 20. At first one attorney and one university professor were members of the club but they afterwards withdrew.

The club met once a month, rotating through the homes of the various members. At each meeting a paper was read on a medical subject of an historical nature. At first the essays covered a wide range, but later emphasis was placed on matters related to American medicine. There was also provision for presentation of clinical case reports. Refreshments, both liquid and solid, followed the discussions. At the beginning of the club the members all dressed in tuxedos, but the whole atmosphere was one of friendship and relaxation.

It is not quite clear who was the first to propose the formation of this group but it was probably Dr. Robert Seibels. Among the early members were Drs. R. W. Gibbes, Heyward Gibbes, Julius Taylor, Floyd Rogers, W. H. Wyman, F. M. Routh, Bruce Edgerton, William Weston, Fred Williams, Hugh Dubose, LeGrand Guerry, and Ralph Foster. After a time formal dress was abandoned and the meetings were somewhat more relaxed. Occasionally meetings were held in hotels, as during World War II when food was rationed.

The club now comprises 22 physicians. While there has been a continuing turnover in the membership, the active members display a considerable enthusiasm, some for the scholarly features and others for the social content.

(Information from Dr. James S. Fouche and Dr. O. B. Mayer, Jr.)

GREENVILLE MEDICAL CLUB

By J. DECHERD GUESS, M.D.

Back in the early twenties before the complete organization of hospital staffs and when there was more time for study and for professional socializing, a need was felt by a group of younger men for a closer affiliation, intercommunication, and for case study. A medical club was organized. It held regular monthly meetings, established a small library of texts of historical interest, and maintained a friendly personal relation among the members. After some years of activity and after the original membership was beginning to age, and organizational demands had become burdensome, the club was destroyed by increasing inertia. Its library was given to the Greenville General Hospital medical library.

The Medico-Chirurgical Club of Charleston

The Medico-Chirurgical Club was organized May 1, 1911 by a group composed of Drs. Albert Nathans, D. L. Maguire, M. S. Moore, R. M. Pollitzer, J. S. Rhame, and W. A. Smith. Its first constitution was adopted May 23, 1911.

The object of the club was to provide for the younger members of the profession an organization in which opinion could be freely expressed, informal consultation asked and given by fellow members, and subjects of practical interest brought up for discussion. Early rules, backed by fines, provided that each member must participate in the discussion of papers, and must never ridicule any obvious error of the essayist, though just criticism was encouraged.

Dr. Nathans was the first secretary-treasurer. At first no president was elected, but the members took turns as chairman at the monthly meetings. Membership was originally limited to twenty, and a steward arranged for the social part of the meetings. Elections were held every six months.

Later the arrangement of officers was changed, and Dr. W. C. O'Driscoll became the first president, January 9, 1912. In this same year it was decided to hold meetings twice a month, and this procedure was followed for four years. In 1916 the meetings in July and August were abandoned.

Programs included many case reports, which were discussed very freely. At one time a series of papers was read on subjects of medical historical interest.

On December 9, 1916, a new constitution was adopted, and an apparently flagging interest of the members was revived. Later, as a result of current world events, the club was inactive from September 18, 1918 to December 2, 1919, when a reorganization took place. In January 1932, the constitution was again revised.

Since 1932, the club has continued to function and has enjoyed sustained popularity. It continues to meet in the Roper Hospital Medical Society Room. Since 1950 the programs have been varied from strictly medical papers. Topics of interest to physicians such as stocks, investments, insurance, sports, and cultural subjects are alternated with medical programs.

Two social events have become traditional. In January, the annual meeting is held at a seafood restaurant where officers are elected for the coming year. This is the annual "Oyster Roast".

In June the annual outdoor barbecue is held.

Since 1958 the membership has remained close to 175 physicians, though only some 35 of these are active. The organization is still "stag"; no women invade the privacy of the male domain.

THE MEDICAL JOURNAL CLUB OF CHARLESTON

The Medical Journal Club of Charleston adopted its constitution and bylaws January 29, 1909 at Roper Hospital. The usual provisions applicable to such an organization were made. The club had 20 members in 1912. It made use of a reading room and elected a librarian who was responsible for the journals which were the subjects of discussion by the members. This club lasted for a number of years.

THE MEDICAL CLUB OF CHARLESTON

Surviving minutes of this defunct club are deposited in the historical library of the Medical University. Perhaps a scrawl on the first page gives a clue to its activities. It says; "½ doz. beer, ½ doz. ale, whiskey, cigars, cigarettes, crackers, cheese, sandwiches". Obviously this was a convivial club, though its interests were avowed to be clinical.

The minutes are handwritten and dated from July 1896 to January 1915. On the first page, a list of the 18 charter members is given. Meetings were held at the Shirras Dispensary office at 72 Society St. Membership was limited to 20. Two meetings a month were held on the first and third Mondays. Membership was by invitation and unanimous election. The club had only one officer, a steward. Absence from four consecutive meetings without valid excuse was cause for expulsion. Funds were accumulated by occasional assessment.

The minutes give a list of subjects of discussions at the meetings. All of these were clinical. On July 3, 1907 it was noted that the annual meeting had been most successful with Dr. J. C. Mitchell as toastmaster, Dr. Lane Mullally as humorist, and with a club song offered by Dr. E. F. Parker.

In 1911 the Medical Club began to hold its meetings at Roper Hospital. The last meeting recorded was that of January 18, 1915.

THE SPARTAN OR SPARTANBURG MEDICAL CLUB

This club was organized in 1915 for the "promotion of medical and surgical advancement". It subscribed to a number of journals and held regular meetings. It was still active in 1917, but apparently disappeared shortly after that time.

CHAPTER 9

MEDICAL PUBLICATIONS IN SOUTH CAROLINA

At the turn of the century there had been no medical journal published in South Carolina since 1877. Dr. Walter Porcher of Charleston, secretary of the Association for 15 years and its president in 1900, recommended then in his address to the Association the establishment of a state journal.

In this proposal he was greatly encouraged and supported by Dr. John L. Dawson. At a time when the Association had only about 311 members, with annual dues of $3.00, this was a rather courageous step to take, and indeed it was not implemented until Dr. Robert Wilson in his presidential address in 1905 suggested again that the *Journal* be established immediately. The House of Delegates was in accord with Dr. Wilson and the *Journal* began its career with Dr. Wilson himself as editor-in-chief. The first number appeared in June 1905 and this and subsequent numbers went through many financial difficulties which the *Journal* managed to survive.

After Dr. Wilson's short term as editor other editors followed, also for relatively short terms. They were Dr. F. H. McLeod, Dr. J. W. Jervey, and Dr. J. C. Sosnowski. In 1912 it was arranged that the secretary, Dr. Edgar A. Hines of Seneca, also function as editor.

In its early issues the articles were mostly by physicians of the state, but gradually the contents became more representative of medicine in general. After the death of Dr. Hines in 1940, Dr. Julian Price of Florence succeeded to the editorial chair and held it until his resignation in 1953, when Dr. Joseph I. Waring of Charleston began his term ending in 1970.

Besides the official *Journal*, during the present century there have been a number of ephemeral publications in the state. One of the earlier was *The Hospital Herald*, a monthly journal of the (Negro) Hospital and Training School in Charleston, edited by Dr. A. C. McClennan, which started publication in 1899 and ran through two volumes. *The Aesculapian*, published by students of the Medical College in 1909, lasted for only four numbers. *The Baker Sanatorium Bulletin* (Charleston) was begun in 1925, but did not persist long. *The McLeod Infirmary Bulletin*, begun in

Florence in 1934 (Dr. Julian Price was editor) survived for only a year or so. *The Bulletin of the Anderson County Hospital,* a monthly publication, was initiated in 1940 and ran for three years with Dr. J. M. Feder as editor.

In June 1937 Dr. Hillyer Rudisill of Charleston inaugurated *The Review of Tumor Therapy,* a monthly publication intended for wide distribution. After a short run of four numbers this was absorbed by *The Southern Surgeon* and eventually disappeared.

In rather recent years several county medical society bulletins have appeared and promise long continuance. *The Recorder* of the Columbia Medical Society was published first in October 1937, under the direction chiefly of Dr. William Weston, Dr. N. B. Heyward, and Dr. T. A. Pitts, and has continued as a successful monthly publication to the present. *The Bulletin of the Greenville County Medical Society,* in which Dr. J. D. Guess, Dr. Everett Poole, and Dr. George Tyler were very active, started as a monthly publication in 1938 and has maintained its pace until now. The Charleston County Society began publication of *The Scribe* in January 1951, and this bulletin continues to appear ten times a year. The monthly *Bulletin of the Pee Dee Medical Association,* instigated and edited by Dr. Joseph Cain, has run since 1948 but lately has been relatively inactive. The most recent special publication is the quarterly *GP News of South Carolina.* Thus, of late, there has been a multiplication of publications and a division of medical interest and talent in a way rather different from that in which matters went sixty five years ago when the *Journal* was founded. Yet all of these journals find interested readers and serve a useful purpose. The *Journal* and *The Recorder* publish scientific material, while the others are devoted primarily to news, announcements, and editorial comment. With as much journalistic interest and experience as is displayed in these publications, there should be ample talent for future developments.

REFERENCES

Joseph I. Waring, M.D., "History of Medical Journalism in South Carolina." *J. S. Carolina Med. Ass.,* 51:185 (June 1955).

Edgar A. Hines, M.D., "The Story of Medical Journalism in South Carolina." *J. S. Carolina Med. Ass.,* 30:66 (April 1934).

Editorial, *J. S. Carolina Med. Ass.,* 1:1 (June 1905).

E. F. Parker, M.D., President's Address. *J. S. Carolina Med. Ass.,* 11:140 (May 1915).

The Recorder OF THE COLUMBIA MEDICAL SOCIETY

The idea of *The Recorder* as the voice of the Columbia Medical Society originated in the mind of Dr. William Weston, Sr. One hot day in July 1937, Dr. T. A. Pitts, Dr. N. B. Heyward, and the president and secretary of the Columbia Medical Society, Dr. W. J. Bristow and Dr. J. M. Davis met with Dr. Weston. He had just returned from a meeting of the American Medical Association where he had seen some county medical society publications and was inspired with the idea of having the Columbia Medical Society put out a publication for the purpose of recording its activities. This committee soon also became enthusiastic about the idea and as a result a publishing committee came into existence composed of Dr. Weston, Dr. Heyward, Dr. Pitts, and the then current president and secretary of the society. Dr. N. B. Heyward was to provide the funds through advertising to print the publication and Dr. Pitts was to edit it. After many trials and tribulations the first issue of *The Recorder*, the name adopted by the society, was published in early October 1937.

The Recorder of the Columbia Medical Society of Richland County was intended to serve as a record of the activities of the society for the information of the absent members and the profession generally. Significant and concisely presented case reports were preserved in its pages, which also carried advance programs for the benefit of other physicians who might care to attend such sessions as particularly interested them. Papers of scientific and historical interest of members of the Columbia Medical Society and their official guests are regular features.

For nine years the three original members of the publishing committee, along with the changing presidents and secretaries published *The Recorder* each month without failure. In January 1946, Dr. George McCutchen took charge as publisher and editor and in February 1947, Dr. Chapman J. Milling succeeded him.

The following editors have served ably since 1947: Dr. Joe Freed, 1948 and 1949; Dr. L. V. Jowers, 1950 and 1951; Dr. P. F. Laborde, 1952 and 1953; Dr. Charles R. Holmes, 1954, 1955, and 1956; Dr. Buford S. Chappell, 1957, 1958, and 1959; Dr. R. P. Watson, 1960; Dr. P. F. LaBorde, 1961; Dr. Buford S. Chappell, 1962 and 1963; Dr. Thomas E. Edwards, 1964 and 1965; Dr. W. W. Ledyard, 1966; Dr. Donald E. Saunders, Jr., 1967 and 1968; Dr. Edward E. Kimbrough, III, 1969 to the present.

On the whole, the business managers have been able to pay all expenses of the publication with the returns from the advertising. When an occasional deficit occurred the Columbia Medical Society made it up.

Publication of *The Recorder* was part of a successful determination to provide the society and its guests with outstanding programs by physicians eminent in their various fields and in the highest office of the AMA. This journal of some 30 pages, appears monthly and is distributed widely over the state.

THE BULLETIN OF THE GREENVILLE COUNTY MEDICAL SOCIETY

In 1937 Dr. Thomas Brockman, newly elected president of the society, aided and assisted by Dr. George Wilkinson, proposed the establishment of a bulletin which would inform members and the profession of the state generally of the activities of the Greenville County Society. The first issue appeared in February 1938 with Dr. J. Decherd Guess as temporary editor. Dr. Guess was followed after two issues by Dr. E. B. Poole and later, Dr. George Tyler and Dr. J. W. Jervey served in the editorial capacity until Dr. Guess was again elected. He continued to serve until 1951.

During the years changes in emphasis in *The Bulletin* have gradually come about as times, circumstances, and editors have changed. For many years the editorials were of considerable interest and of fancied or real value in moulding medical opinion. It seems that there was more controversy in those earlier days, particularly in connection with the expansion program of the Medical College. More recently *The Bulletin* has served principally as a news organ of the society.

As with similar publications, the onus of producing *The Bulletin* rested firmly on the editor, although a publication committee stood by with approbation but relatively little assistance. A co-editor and a business manager were appointed and eased the burden of the editor. The publication was not intended primarily to be a source of scientific information but rather a house organ which would knit the members of the society closer. It has existed on its advertising revenue with occasional assistance from the society. It circulates largely over the state and elsewhere with a mailing list of more than 1,600.

THE PEE DEE BULLETIN OF THE PEE DEE MEDICAL ASSOCIATION

The first issue of the monthly *Pee Dee Bulletin* appeared in February 1948 with Dr. Joseph P. Cain, Jr. as editor. He continued until December 1958 when Dr. Harold Gilmore became editor, and he was succeeded by Dr. Ira Barth in 1961. Of late publication has been irregular, but it is hoped that the *Bulletin* can be revived.

The Scribe OF THE CHARLESTON MEDICAL SOCIETIES

This modest bulletin intended for local and statewide distribution was developed after some planning and made its first appearance in January 1951, with Dr. Joseph I. Waring as editor and Dr. John Arthur Siegling as it financial advisor.

The Scribe made no pretense at carrying scientific material, but attempted to serve as a bulletin of news, programs, opinions, and information of activities in the local medical world. There were occasional ventures into bits of doggerel and anecdotes of various kinds. Like all good Charlestonians, it slows its activity during the hot weather so that no issues of an otherwise monthly publication appeared in the summer. Publication has continued without interruption since the first number appeared.

In 1954 Dr. Harold Pettit became editor and in 1969 Dr. A. L. Lemel was made his assistant. *The Scribe* continues regular publication. Dr. Lemel achieved the editorship in 1970.

MISCELLANEOUS BULLETINS

The earliest bulletin of the state was the South Carolina Medical Association's Councillor's *Bulletin* which appeared bi-monthly. It was in publication in 1905 and perhaps for some time later.

The McLeod Infirmary Bulletin appeared first in 1934 with Dr. Julian Price as editor and appeared for a few years. This was a quarterly bulletin and contained only scientific articles.

The Bulletin of the Anderson County Hospital was published first in 1939 but survived for a rather short period. Volume 1 was published with Dr. J. M. Feder as editor. This was a monthly publication which ran to three or more volumes and contained only scientific articles.

The GP News of South Carolina, an organ of the South Carolina Chapter of the Academy of General Practice, began publication in 1963 under the editorship of Dr. Harold Jeter and has continued to appear to the present. It is essentially a news bulletin with a few scientific articles included.

The *Alumni Bulletin* of the Medical University of South Carolina began in 1943 as a mimeographed publication promoted by Miss Annabelle Furman of the Medical College Library and Dr. J. I. Waring, chairman of the Library Committee. In April of 1944 the first issue of the second volume assumed magazine form and the *Bulletin* has been appearing quarterly since that time as a product of the Alumni Association office. Mrs. Joan Bamberg acted as editor from 1955 to 1967. Lately the *Bulletin* has been under the direction of Miss Ruth Barker, Executive Secretary of the Alumni Association.

CHAPTER 10

POSTGRADUATE ORGANIZATIONS

THE SOUTHERN PEDIATRIC SEMINAR

The Southern Pediatric Seminar, a postgraduate course in pediatrics held in the summer months, was the result of the combined interest and efforts of Dr. D. Lesesne Smith of Spartanburg and Dr. Frank H. Richardson of Black Mountain, North Carolina. The need for such postgraduate courses and the determination to arrange them had been in the minds of these two pediatricians long before the seminar was started in 1920. Both of the founders were aware of the high mortality of children in the South, especially from diarrheal diseases and suspected that much of it might be due to a lack of a modern knowledge of pediatrics on the part of the general practitioner. The seminar was designed to widen this knowledge and in its course it succeeded eminently well, primarily because of the dedication of Dr. Smith.

The faculty of the seminar was made up of most of the eminent pediatricians of the South, who served without pay and came year after year to Saluda, a small town just over the North Carolina border, where Dr. Smith had his own private hospital for children and also conducted there a charity institution, the Spartanburg Baby Hospital, which was supported by the people of Spartanburg.

The operation in Saluda was a family affair with Dr. Smith the moving spirit and his children and members of their families faithful and efficient assistants. After the death of Dr. Smith in 1947, Dr. Lesesne Smith, Jr., took on the responsibility as registrar and program chairman.

Over its 38 years of life the seminar accommodated some three or four thousand doctors, some of whom returned many times, as the program was varied each year. The first session of the seminar had 16 lecturers and five registered students, but grew rapidly to the point of registering 75 to 125 attendants each summer. Dr. William Mulherin was dean of the seminar. Later Dr. Samuel F. Ravenel of Greensboro succeeded him and in turn was succeeded by Dr. Julian Price and then by Dr. Warren Quillian.

In the first year, two days of the time allotted were spent in Black Mountain where Dr. Richardson had his clinic, but thereafter all the courses were given at Saluda and were held in a large tent until a lecture hall could be constructed. Later in the history of the seminar, instruction in obstetrics and gynecology was added to the curriculum and, after 1954, two days were devoted to internal medicine. A distinguished faculty continued to give its services to the cause without compensation.

In 1957 the name was change to the Southern Postgraduate Seminar. Recreation and entertainment were not unimportant parts of the stay on Smith Hill.

In 1930 the Commonwealth Fund gave a contribution of $2,000 to be used for paying the expenses of doctors over 41 years of age who practiced in small towns. This and another $500 grant from the Doris Duke Foundation in 1951 were the only financial aid the seminar ever received.

In 1958 the Spartanburg Baby Hospital was closed and other pediatric refresher courses and postgraduate sessions were becoming widely available. When it seemed that the seminar had outlived its usefulness, it was decided that an institution which had been a most valuable one would close its doors.

Piedmont Postgraduate Clinical Assembly

In 1935 a series of highly successful obstetrical institutes were held throughout the state by Dr. J. R. McCord of Atlanta in an effort to lower the unhappy record of obstetrical mortality in the state. One of the results of this series was the formation of the Piedmont Postgraduate Clinical Assembly, which arose from a feeling that postgraduate medical education was badly needed in the state generally as well as in the area about Anderson.

Dr. Edgar A. Hines of Seneca, at that time serving as administrator of the Anderson County Hospital, with other interested physicians, instigated the development of an assembly to which the doctors from surrounding counties of South Carolina and adjacent counties in Georgia were to be invited. This meeting extended over three days and allowed time for some relaxation. Prominent speakers from the South Atlantic states were invited to participate. From the very beginning the Assembly enjoyed an attendance well above the 100 mark, and has continued to grow over the years to its present size.

A request that the problem of cancer be given special consideration led to the practice of inviting guests to speak on that subject. Programs now include various branches of medicine. The institution is listed by the Council on Medical Education and Hospitals of the American Medical Association.

SUMMER MEDICAL SCHOOLS IN CHARLESTON

A Charleston Summer Medical Institute was established by Middleton Michel as early as 1848 and was in existence until the Civil War. It is not clear whether the Charleston Medical School which was in existence as late as 1907 was a continuation of the early school or its successor. In February of 1907 the Charleston Medical School gave up its conduct of the teaching service in Roper Hospital and the South Carolina Postgraduate Medical School was organized and acquired the same privileges. The name of this school was changed soon to the Roper Hospital Polyclinic Medical School, also mentioned as the Polyclinic School of Medicine and Surgery of the Roper Hospital. The school was continued until June 6, 1913 when its operation was abandoned.

These schools were conducted by the members of the Medical Society of South Carolina, operated in the summer, and included in their faculties many of those who were on the teaching staff of the Medical College of the State of South Carolina. Among them were Dr. Robert Wilson, Dr. C. P. Aimar, Dr. A. J. Buist, Dr. Robert Cathcart, Dr. T. Prioleau Whaley, Dr. Walter Peyre Porcher, Dr. A. E. Baker, Dr. Lane Mullally, Dr. Austin Ball, and Dr. Edward Rutledge. The courses were varied and inclusive, ranging from pathology, bacteriology, surgery, and pediatrics, to dermatology. The school operated in a frame building on Lucas Street (Barre Street) facing Mill Street, just north of the Roper Hospital Building of 1906. Election of the faculty was by a majority vote of the Medical Society members. The scheme for the establishment of the school proposed that each elected faculty member should put up a certain sum of money to cover expenses until the institution should prove self-supporting.

REFRESHER COURSE AT THE MEDICAL COLLEGE

Celebration of Founders Day at the Medical College was inaugurated in 1934. The proceedings consisted of one day of clinics and demonstrations by faculty members and an evening banquet.

In 1942, at the instigation and under the direction of the Alumni Association of the Medical College, a more ambitious refresher course was instituted at the College. It was conducted by eminent guest speakers in connection with the observance of Founders Day.

Over the years it varied from one to three days in duration and occasionally had adjunct programs attached. This course was promoted largely by Dr. James Fouche and Dr. Strother Pope, with the assistance of a number of other vitally interested alumni. Under the management of the Alumni Association, it prospered for a number of years. In 1948, it seemed to have had a slump, but in subsequent years it came back to its original activity. In 1949, the interest and attendance were considerably better. Shortly after this time, the management of the course was assumed by the Medical College and continued under its auspices. A gradual decline in interest led to its abandonment in 1966.

CHAPTER 11

BIOGRAPHIES OF THE PRESIDENTS OF THE SOUTH CAROLINA MEDICAL ASSOCIATION AND OTHERS

ROBERT EPHRAIM ABELL
1887-1963

Dr. Abell was born at Lowrys, S. C. where he pursued his preparatory education. He then attended the Presbyterian College

of South Carolina for one year and Davidson College for two years. His degree in medicine was conferred by the University of Maryland School of Medicine in 1912. After graduation he served as resident surgeon at University Hospital, Baltimore, 1912-1915.

He returned to Chester and immediately became interested in the establishment of the Chester Sanatorium, of which he was surgeon in charge as well as treasurer and manager. He was also visiting surgeon of the Memorial Hospital in Abbeville and and surgeon in charge of Pryor Hospital, Chester. He retired from practice in 1939.

During the first World War he was commissioned a first lieutenant of the Medical Corps and served in France with Evacuation Hospital Number 26; he was promoted to captain before his discharge in 1919. Dr. Abell was a fellow of the American College of Surgeons and a member of the State Board of Medical Examiners. He contributed a number of papers to the meetings of the Seaboard Railroad Surgeons and engaged in many civic activities.

CHARLES RICHARD FURMAN BAKER
1902-

Dr. Baker, the son and grandson of doctors, was born and raised in Sumter. His father was Dr. Samuel Chandler Baker who in 1909 was president of the South Carolina Medical Association. A graduate of the Episcopal High School in Virginia, he completed his academic (B.S.) and medical degrees at the University of Virginia (1926). Surgical training in New York at St. Luke's and New York Hospitals followed. For a short time he was assistant to Dr. R. L. Ramey in El Paso, Texas but in 1931 he returned to Sumter to practice surgery.

He is a fellow of the American College of Surgeons and is certified by the American Board of Surgery, a charter member of the South Carolina Surgical Society and once its president. In the South Carolina Medical Association he was a member of Council for nine years and was active in the establishment of Blue Shield in the state.

SAMUEL CHANDLER BAKER
1866-1918

Son of Dr. C. R. F. Baker, and a native of Sumter County, Dr. Baker graduated from Davidson College (A.B. 1886), taught school

for a year, and after preliminary preparation in Charlottesville, attained his medical degree at the University of Virginia in 1888. He then was associated in Sumter with Dr. J. J. Bossard, and continued his practice there until his death.

In 1894, with Dr. A. C. Dick, he established the 10 bed Baker-Dick Infirmary, which became the Sumter Hospital and later the Tuomey Hospital. His special activity was in surgery. He helped to organize the Sumter County Medical Association and served several times as its president. He was a member of the State Board of Medical Examiners for ten years, was elected a member of the Council of the South Carolina Medical Association in 1907, and after serving as secretary, he was elected president of the Association in 1908.[1] He was a member of the American College of Surgeons, one of the first from South Carolina. Active in the Tri-State Medical Association, he was its vice-president and member of its council. He was a member of the board of regents of the State Hospital for the Insane.

Dr. Baker worked hard to establish Red Cross chapters in his section of the state. In World War I he volunteered and was made a captain. While taking special training in New York he developed the pneumonia which was to terminate his outstanding career.

REFERENCE
1. Editorial, *J. S. Carolina Med. Ass.*, 4:219 (May 1908).

WILLIAM THOMAS BROCKMAN
1881-1968

Born at Reidville in Spartanburg County, William Thomas Brockman moved to Greer and later to Greenville, where he established

himself as a specialist in proctology. In his early days he had become interested in medicine and served as a semi-apprentice to a busy practitioner at Reidville. Later he spent some time at Furman University and after one year at the Atlanta Medical College, he entered the Medical College of the State of South Carolina and graduated in 1909, thereafter serving an internship in Roper Hospital.

Settling in Greer, he followed a general practice for 14 years before adopting his specialty. Becoming concerned with the need for proper proctological treatment among his patients, he pursued a number of short courses in his chosen specialty, a procedure which he continued to follow for many years.

While in Greer he participated in local political activities and served as mayor for three years; he followed his civic interests in Greenville and was a member of its city council for several terms.

He became a fellow of the American Proctological Society, which honored him in 1957. He was chairman of the Section on Proctology of the Southern Medical Association. He served on the Council of the South Carolina Medical Association for some years. Specializing in proctology in 1926, he became the first exponent of that discipline in the state. In 1932 he moved to Greenville. He held the position of president of the Greenville County Medical Society and was very active in furthering its welfare, especially in promoting publication of the Greenville *Bulletin* and in building local programs which added much to the efficacy of the organization.

Thomas Brockman was a medical leader, a man of much magnetism, a kindly friendly person with a profound concern with religion and civic welfare. Many people sought his wise counsel on many subjects.

REFERENCE

J. Decherd Guess, M.D., *A Medical History of Greenville County, South Carolina* (Greenville: Greenville County Medical Society, 1959), pp. 52-58.

ROBERT COLUMBUS BRUCE

1877-1944

Robert Columbus Bruce was born in Kershaw County on July 29, 1877. After attending local schools, then The Citadel, where

he graduated in 1896, he taught school for six years in Newberry. He then entered the Vanderbilt University School of medicine, and graduated with the M.D. degree in 1910.

Dr. Bruce located in Greenville and soon built up a large practice. He was a careful, well-trained doctor with a friendly personality which drew and bound people to him in an unusual manner. He remained in active general practice until a few days before his death.

Because of his lovable character, sound judgment, and his interest in the better things of organized medicine, many honors were conferred upon Dr. Bruce. He served the Greenville County Medical Society in all its offices. He served as Councillor for the Fourth District of the state medical association for ten years, and in 1935 he was named president-elect of the Association. Upon the death of Dr. Harmon while in office, he assumed the presidency, and was officially installed in 1936.

Dr. Bruce was a charter member of the staffs of the Greenville General and the St. Francis hospitals. He was a chief of the medical service of the former from its beginning, and for many years he was a member of its medical (executive) committee. Wherever he served he became the "trouble shooter", and he smoothed out many wrangles, and unraveled many snarls, by virtue of his understanding, sincerity, patience, and wisdom. At the time of his death, he was chairman of the city Board of Health. During World War I he was chief medical examiner for the local draft board, serving with patriotic devotion in that capacity.

GEORGE HENRY BUNCH
1879-1950

A native of Edgefield, Dr. Bunch spent his life in Columbia and was nationally known as a distinguished surgeon and locally

esteemed as a beloved citizen of his adopted city. He went through the lower schools of Columbia and achieved the degree of A.B. at the University of South Carolina (then the South Carolina College) in 1899, then proceeding to the University of Michigan, where he became a doctor of medicine in 1903. He did a short stint of practice in a mining community before returning to Columbia to become associated with Dr. Arthur E. Shaw in general practice, and later with Dr. LeGrand Guerry. Subsequently he confined his activity to surgery.

He was chief of staff at the Baptist Hospital, the Columbia Hospital, and Providence Hospital. He also served as consulting surgeon to the tuberculosis sanatorium at State Park and to the Southern Railway. He was the first president of the South Carolina Surgical Society and a member of the Southern Surgical Association.

Dr. Bunch was an able writer on technical subjects and also interested himself very much in medical history and the cultural side of medicine, as evidenced by his membership in the Columbia Medical Club. He was physically very active, playing a good game of tennis until the very last days of his life. The Columbia Medical Society elected him its president, as did the Tri-State Medical Association. A fellow of the American College of Surgeons and a member of the International College of Surgeons, he was also a diplomate of the American Board of Surgery and a member of its founding group. His surgical skill and personal kindness, along with his many worthy civic activities, endeared him to the people of Columbia.

JOSEPH PALMER CAIN, JR.
1912-1971

Dr. Cain, a member of a family long involved in medicine, was born in Greenville, S. C., August 6, 1912. He achieved the B.S.

degree at the University of South Carolina in 1931 and the M.D. degree at the Medical College of the State of South Carolina in 1935. He served internships at St. Francis Infirmary in Charleston and at Lynn Hospital in Lynn, Massachusetts, and residencies in the Mission Hospital in Asheville and the Mullins Hospital. He pursued postgraduate courses at George Washington University and at the Medical College of South Carolina.

Active in the practice of medicine and surgery in Mullins since 1937, he was chief of staff at the Mullins Hospital, and on the consultant staff at the Marion County Hospital and the St. Eugene Hospital at Dillon. His activities in organized medicine have been very numerous and he held many positions, such as president of the Marion County Medical Society and of the Pee Dee Medical Association, whose *Bulletin* he edited from 1948 to 1958. He was a member of the Council of the South Carolina Medical Association for ten years and served as chairman for five years preceding his nomination as president-elect in 1959. He was a member of the editorial board of *The Journal of the South Carolina Medical Association,* was a member of the Committee on Industrial Health of the American Medical Association, and a member of the Southeastern Surgical Congress. He was a director of the South Carolina Medical Care Plan (Blue

Shield), and was active in its establishment. He was surgical consultant to the South Carolina Division of Vocational Rehabilitation, and received a Congressional citation for work as examining physician with the Marion County Draft Board No. 1 in World War II. He was a trustee of the Medical University of South Carolina.

Dr. Cain was also vitally involved in the Alumni Association of the Medical University, serving once as its president, and did much to promote interest in postgraduate education. He was also deeply concerned in the development of the branch of the University of South Carolina at Florence, and gave much time to civic work of many kinds, serving on his town council and interesting himself in many local activities.

Dr. Cain rendered valuable and important service during his term as delegate to the American Medical Association from the South Carolina Medical Association.

ROBERT SPANN CATHCART
1871-1949

Dr. Cathcart, long a leading surgeon of Charleston, was a native of Columbia, where he graduated in 1890 from the School of

Pharmacy of the University before achieving his medical degree at the Medical College of the State of South Carolina in 1893. He subsequently pursued postgraduate study at various clinics.

Beginning in general practice in Charleston, he eventually devoted himself strictly to surgery, in which he became nationally prominent. He was a member of the American College of Surgeons, being on its Board of Governors, and of the Southern Surgical Association, which he served as president. He was surgeon to the Atlantic Coast Line and Seaboard Railway, and president of both of the surgeons' societies of these railroads, chief surgeon at Roper Hospital and at The Citadel, and head of the department of surgery of the Medical College. He was a devoted promoter and supporter of the Roper Hospital. He attained the presidential chair in the Tri-State Medical Association and the South Carolina Medical Association.

During World War I he began service as a lieutenant, was promoted to major, and later to lieutenant colonel in the Reserve. He acted as medical advisor to the governor of South Carolina and later served in army hospitals.

In addition to his duties in teaching, Dr. Cathcart had a large private practice. His contributions to the Roper Hospital were recognized gratefully by the Medical Society of South Carolina, which commissioned a portrait now hanging in the hospital and presented him with a silver pitcher. He received the Algernon Sydney Sullivan award from The Citadel.

Dr. Cathcart was the author of numerous articles on surgical subjects.

OLIN BURNHAM CHAMBERLAIN
1892-1968

Olin Chamberlain, a native of Charleston, was a graduate of the College of Charleston and first honor graduate of the Medical College of the State of South Carolina (1918). After hospital experience at the Philadelphia General Hospital and at Roper Hospital he entered private practice, later confining himself to internal medicine and finally to nervous and mental diseases. He became a professor of biology and also of psychology at the College of Charleston and eventually professor of neuro-psychiatry at the Medical College, serving also as first director of its Mental Hygiene Clinic.

Dr. Chamberlain did postgraduate work at the National Hospital for the Paralyzed and Epileptic in London and at Harvard University Medical School. He was a member of many medical organizations and served as a visiting physician at Roper Hospital. In 1962 his portrait was unveiled in the psychiatric department of the Medical College. He served for some time as a member of the board of the State Hospital. He was a fellow of the American College of Physicians and a diplomate of the American Board of Internal Medicine.

During World War II he spent two years in the army medical corps and was chief of the neuropsychiatric service at Bushnell General Hospital in Utah, where he attained the rank of colonel.

Olin Chamberlain was a man of extraordinary intelligence and ability. He combined a keen mind with a lively sense of humor and an affable personality. As he became involved in the newer developments in psychiatry he kept his feet firmly on the ground, giving much sound help to his many appreciative patients. His friends were many and intimate and shared with him the enjoyment of a life full of pleasant amenities as well as more serious concerns. He was a man of the outdoors, a welcomed member in any group, social, professional, or literary, and a true student of his profession.

Dr. Chamberlain died on June 30, 1968 after a long hospital stay. He had been retired and had suffered varying degrees of ill health since 1952.

ROBERT LAFAYETTE CRAWFORD
1898-

After completing the public schools of Lancaster, his native town, Dr. Crawford attended the University of South Carolina in 1915-

1919, spending six months of his last scholastic year in the Reserve Officers Training Camp at Plattsburg, N. Y. He was commissioned second lieutenant and served at Pittsburgh. Entering the Medical College of the State of South Carolina, he graduated in 1923, served internships at Roper Hospital for two years, and then began general practice in Lancaster. He continued his preparation with work at the Postgraduate Medical School in New York and the Bellevue-Columbia Postgraduate School.

Dr. Crawford was active in medical affairs in the state, and served as chairman of the Section on General Practice of the

American Medical Association. He has held membership in many medical organizations. He enjoys immense popularity in his home town and was honored by having his portrait commissioned by his many friends. The respect of his fellow practitioners was shown by his election as first chief of staff when the Marion Sims Memorial Hospital was opened. He was president of the South Carolina Academy of General Practice and delegate to the national body. Dr. Crawford has had many civic and charitable efforts to his credit.

He comes from one of the oldest families in Lancaster County. His grandfather, a physician, was a signer of the South Carolina Ordinance of Secession and was killed in the medical service in the Confederate Army. Medicine has been the occupation of a number of other members of the family.

THEODORE GAILLARD CROFT, JR.
1845-1915

Born in Greenville, Dr. Croft spent most of his life in Aiken. He attended Furman University. During the Civil War he was a non-commissioned officer, serving as sergeant of the 16th S. C. Volunteers for one year, and from 1862-1865 he was connected with The Citadel.

After the close of the war he resumed his schooling, attending the University of Virginia, and afterward graduating in 1875 from the Medical College of the State of South Carolina. He then settled in Aiken and devoted 40 years of his life to his practice, which yielded great satisfaction to this affable, courteous, and cheerful Christian gentleman.

In spite of an active practice, he found time to contribute papers to the state medical journal, to serve as chairman of the Board of Health of Aiken, to pursue activity in the Association of Surgeons of the Southern Railway, and to act as Councillor from the Eighth District of the South Carolina Medical Association. He also gave his services on two stints as trustee of the Medical College and served on the State Board of Medical Examiners. Besides these activities, Dr. Croft also pursued an interest in the field of politics and in his religious activities, and served as surgeon to the First Regiment of South Carolina Volunteers after the Civil War.

DRAYTON MARGART CROSSON
1858-1936

Born in Prosperity, S. C. Dr. Crosson attended the local schools, working during the summers to provide funds for his education.

He then spent three years at Erskine College, afterward going to the Medical College of the State of South Carolina for two years and finally transferring to the Medical Department of the University of Nashville, where he achieved his medical degree with first honors in 1883. Afterward he frequently pursued postgraduate courses to maintain his current knowledge of medicine.

His general practice began at Lewiedale. Subsequently he removed to Leesville, where he spent the rest of his life. In addition to being an able physician and a militant opponent of quackery, he served as mayor of Leesville six times and was a state senator. Agriculture occupied much of his interest, and he carried on large farming operations as well as a busy practice.

EDWARD FRANCIS DARBY
1860-1906

A native of Magnolia, S. C., son of a physician, he attended
Holy Communion Church Institute in Charleston and the Virginia
Military Academy. He was graduated from Kings Mountain Mili-
tary Academy at York in 1879. Under the preceptorship of Dr.
B. W. Taylor and Dr. A. N. Talley, he commenced the study of
medicine and attended the Medical College of the State of South
Carolina and the University of Louisville School of Medicine in
Louisville, Kentucky, and finally receiving his degree from the
University of Maryland School of Medicine in 1884. He was vice-
president of the Sumter County Medical Society and contributed
a number of medical papers as well as a small book on "Advice to
Mothers". He practiced medicine in Lynchburg and Magnolia.
Later he removed to Columbia.

JOHN LAWRENCE DAWSON
1859-1917

Born in Charleston, Dr. Dawson had his early schooling under the well-known teacher Augustus Sachtleben. In 1878 he received

the degree of B.A. from the College of Charleston and in 1881 he became M.D. at the Medical College of the State of South Carolina. At the same time the College of Charleston conferred on him the degree of master of arts.

After graduation he assisted in the anatomy department of the Medical College and was elected demonstrator of anatomy in 1887. Three years later he was elevated to the chair of Practice and Clinical Medicine, which position he held until forced by ill health to resign in 1903. For two years after that he served as assistant physician at the Loomis Sanitarium in New York, there devoting himself to a special study of tuberculosis.

Complete restoration of his health allowed him to return to Charleston and resume practice. He was a member of the Board of Commissioners of the Roper Hospital and professor of the practice of medicine in the Roper Hospital Polyclinic School. Presidency of the Medical Society of South Carolina came to him in 1908. He was a member of the Board of Health of the City of Charleston.

Dr. Dawson was a man naturally gifted with unusual intelligence and a thorough academic training. He reached a rare degree of intellectul attainment and professional achievement.

GEORGE ROSWELL DEAN
1844-1911

A native of Anderson County, he attended Furman University briefly, then removed to The Citadel, which he left to enter the

Confederate Army and to which he returned after the end of the War. He then taught school while studying under a medical preceptor before entering the Medical College of the State of South Carolina, where he spent two years, then removed to Jefferson Medical College, graduating in 1868. Shortly afterward he married and began to practice general medicine at Campton, near Spartanburg, at the same time conducting farming operations. He was a member of the state legislature at one time but found no particular interest in politics. In the early nineties he removed to Spartanburg where he became a prominent citizen concerned with civic and educational affairs and was one of the founders of Converse College. He was considered the head of the medical profession in Spartanburg and practiced as an able surgeon with emphasis on abdominal operations. His concern was largely responsible for the organization of the Spartanburg City Hospital. He served as chairman of the executive committee of the State Board of Health, vice-president of the Southern Medical Association, vice-president of the Pan-American Medical Association, and president of the Association of Surgeons of the Southern Railway Company.

"He was alert in his wide and accurate knowledge of medical science and surgery, but in his love for humanity, his fidelity to duty, and his sympathy for suffering, he remained to the last a doctor of the old school." *

---

* From biographical sketch written by Dr. Dean's grandson Dr. George D. Johnson.

JAMES HENRY DesPORTES
1879 (1880?)-1947

James DesPortes was born at Ridgeway and was a graduate of the Medical College of the State of South Carolina in 1900. After graduation he served in hospitals in Mexico and later engaged in work on malaria in South Carolina. During the first World War he was physician at the Port Terminals at Charleston and a colonel on the medical staff of the South Carolina Militia. He served his local school board as a trustee and also held that position at the Medical College for some time.

Dr. DesPortes spent the greatest part of his life in general practice in Fort Mill. He was president of the York County Medical Society and represented his district on the Council of the South Carolina Medical Association, serving as chairman for several years.

Dr. DesPortes was known as a man of firm character with a strong trait of perseverance and a large and generous heart.

ROBERT BLAKELY DURHAM
1892-1957

A native of Orangeburg County, Dr. Durham attended the South Carolina Co-Educational Institute at Edgefield and received his M.D. degree from the University of Georgia School of Medicine in 1913. He first practiced in Perry, South Carolina, but moved to Columbia early in 1915. Shortly thereafter he volunteered for service in the Army and was commissioned as first lieutenant, serving in France with distinction and honor for nearly two years, first as battalion surgeon in the 101st Infantry and later as commander of the 102nd Ambulance Corps. He was promoted to the rank of captain, and while in France attended the University of Bordeaux for some months, taking a special course in surgery.

He then resumed practice in Columbia and was medical director of the U. S. Veteran's Bureau until the completion of the Veteran's Hospital, at which time he resigned to devote himself entirely to surgery. He retired in June 1955.

Dr. Durham was a fellow of the American College of Surgeons and president of the Columbia Medical Society. He was immensely popular and devoted himself to the high ideals of his profession.

NORMAN OLIN EADDY
1908-

Dr. Eaddy of Sumter, son of a physician, was born in Timmonsville on December 23, 1908. He attended the University of North Carolina in 1925-26, the College of Charleston in 1926-27, and the Medical College of the State of South Carolina, graduating there in 1931. He served a rotating internship at the U. S. Marine Hospital, San Francisco 1931-1932. He was engaged in general practice in South Carolina in 1933-1934. He then served a residency in ear, nose, and throat at Brooklyn Eye and Ear Hospital, Brooklyn, N. Y. in 1935-1936, and a residency in ophthalmology at the Episcopal Eye, Ear, and Throat Hospital, Washington, D. C. in 1936-1937 for a total period of 30 months.

He has practiced his specialty in diseases of the eye, ear, nose, and throat in Sumter 1937-1942 and from 1946 until the present. From 1942 to 1946 he was in the U. S. Army Air Corps, entering as a captain, and separating as a major.

He is a member of a number of medical societies in the state, a licentiate of the American Board of Ophthalmology, and a fellow of the Academy of Ophthalmology and Otolaryngology.

CURRAN BERTRAM EARLE
1875-1944

Dr. Curran Earle was born in Anderson County, the son of a well known physician. He graduated A.B. at Furman University in 1892 and at the University of Maryland he obtained his medical degree in 1896. He then served some time in the University Hospital and in the Woman's Hospital in Baltimore, afterwards pursuing postgraduate work.

Dr. Earle located in Greenville, where he became president of the Greenville County Medical Society. He confined his work to surgery and was a charter member of the American College of Surgeons. He wrote a number of medical papers. With his father, J. B. Earle, and a cousin, T. T. Earle, he established one of Greenville's first hospitals, known as the Greenville Sanatorium. During World War I he served as a major at Camp Wadsworth. Later he was a railway surgeon in Greenville. For one year he was managing editor of the *Journal of the South Carolina Medical Association*.

Dr. Earle engaged in many civic activities. He was a man of firm convictions and outspoken opinion, of strong likes and dislikes, a man of unquestioned integrity, who quietly gave help to many people.

WILLIAM EGLESTON
1873-1935

A native of Winnsboro, Dr. Egleston pursued his higher education at the University of the South and graduated in medicine from

the medical department of the University of Nashville in 1898. He taught anatomy for a time at the Sewanee Medical College. Later he attended the Medical College of the State of South Carolina.

He practiced two years at Barnwell before settling at Hartsville in a general practice, maintaining a constant interest in the promotion of preventive medicine. He interested himself in the eradication of mosquitoes in his home town and was for more than 25 years a member of the Executive Committee of the State Board of Health and its chairman in 1931.

Dr. Egleston served as a medical officer at Camp Lee, Va. in World War I. He was a railroad surgeon, physician to Coker College, and a member of the Hartsville Board of Health. He also concerned himself with the management of county affairs and pursued a banking career as a sideline to his primary interest. Always interested in organized medicine, he worked hard but quietly for its betterment. His contemporaries spoke of his charm and the tender compassion and loving sympathy which he bestowed on his patients. He was a member of a number of outstanding organizations such as the Society of the Cincinnati, the New England Society, and the Huguenot Society, and was a Mason and a Shriner.

DAVIS FURMAN
1859-1931

Dr. Furman was born in Greenville and spent most of his life there. He attended briefly the school of medicine at the University of Louisville and graduated from the University of Maryland in 1882. After practicing for a short time in Missouri and Tennessee he returned to his native town.

Dr. Furman was a member of the Executive Committee of the State Board of Health and chairman of the Greenville County Board of Health. He served as president of the Tri-State Medical Association and was always much interested in the activities of organized medicine. He was also particularly concerned with pellagra and was the writer of a number of medical papers on various subjects. He had an acute interest in community affairs.

THOMAS RUCKER GAINES
1895-

Born in Hart County, Ga., Dr. Gaines was educated in the local schools and at Gibson-Mercer Academy in Bowman, Ga. He received his medical degree from Emory University in 1916. After service in the Medical Corps, U. S. Army, on the Mexican Border and in World War I, 1916-1919, he engaged in general practice in Hartwell, Ga., until 1925, after which he pursued postgraduate work in diseases of the eye, ear, nose, and throat at New Orleans. Since 1927 he has been in the specialized practice of ophthalmology and otolaryngology at Anderson, except for three years spent in the Army Medical Corps during World War II.

Dr. Gaines is a fellow of the American College of Surgeons and a fellow of the American Academy of Ophthalmology and Otolaryngology.

JAMES HILL GRESSETTE
1913-

Dr. Gressette was born in St. Matthews in 1913 and there he completed his secondary school education. He graduated from the

University of South Carolina in 1934, and from the Medical College of the State of South Carolina in 1938. He served his internship at the Macon Hospital, Macon, Ga., and was a resident and later an associate in ophthalmology and otolaryngology at the Gill Memorial Hospital in Roanoke, Va. Dr. Gressette is a licentiate of the Board of Ophthalmology and the Board of Otolaryngology, is a fellow of the American College of Surgeons, and of the International College of Surgeons.

He has been active in his local medical society and in the affairs of his community, as well as in organized medicine of the state. He is a past president of the Edisto Medical Society, and past chief of staff of the Orangeburg Regional Hospital. He has served as president of the Orangeburg Chamber of Commerce and the Orangeburg Rotary Club. He is a director of the Bank of Orangeburg, and president of the Industrial Development Corporation of Orangeburg.

Dr. Gressette is a past president of the South Carolina Society of Ophthalmology and Otolaryngology. He served on the Council of the South Carolina Medical Association for nine years, was chairman of the Council in 1960-1961, and president of the Association in 1963.

LeGRAND GUERRY
1873-1947

Born in Florence, Dr. Guerry attended schools in Summerville and later went to the University of the South at Sewanee. His

medical degree was obtained from the University of Georgia Medical College in 1896. After graduation he served in the City Hospital in Augusta, then pursued postgraduate courses in Baltimore, and did some brief practice before removing to Columbia in 1899. In 1918 he served in the Volunteer Medical Service Corps.

After a short period of general practice he limited his activity to surgery, in which branch of medicine he became nationally known. He was the chief surgeon of his area of the state, and often traveled far to perform "kitchen surgery". He was vice-president of the American Surgical Association, a charter member of the American College of Surgeons, a member of the founders group and a diplomate of the American Board of Surgery, president of the Southern Surgical Association, of the Columbia Medical Society, of the Tri-State Medical Association, and of the Southern Medical Association. While in Augusta he carried on some teaching in the University of Georgia Medical College.

He received many honors: the degree of doctor of civil law from the University of the South in 1924, doctor of laws from the University of South Carolina in 1928, doctor of science from the University of Georgia in 1931, and honorary Phi Beta Kappa membership from the University of the South in 1926. For many years deeply interested in the Columbia Hospital, where a wing was named for him and a plaque in his honor placed on the wall, he became its chief surgeon. A bust presented by his admiring colleagues is in the hospital.

Dr. Guerry wrote many papers, nearly all of them related to surgical subjects. He was particularly interested in appendicitis, and established certain techniques which were widely imitated. He followed the practice of associating himself annually with the outstanding surgeons at the Johns Hopkins Hospital.

Civic affairs interested him as did many others. A handsome man of athletic physique, an active sportsman, much interested in horticulture, a bibliophile, and a student of the Bible and Shakespeare, he was for some years senior warden of the Good Shepherd Episcopal Church in Columbia and president of the board of the Young Men's Christian Association.

JOSEPH DECHERD GUESS
1891-

At the age of nine years, Dr. Guess moved from his birthplace in Free Stone County, Texas to South Carolina. He received his

B.S. degree from the College of Charleston in 1911, taught school for two years in Spartanburg, and then completed his medical education at the Medical College of the State of South Carolina in 1917. Some ten years later he pursued postgraduate work in obstetrics and gynecology at the University of Pennsylvania.

After an internship in Roper Hospital, he served in the Army Medical Corps for two years before locating in practice in Greenville in 1919. There he has been prominent in many activities of a civic and cultural nature and has been an outstanding figure in obstetrics and gynecology, as well as a vitally interested member of the South Carolina Medical Association. He has served as president of the Greenville County Medical Society and was one of the founders and a president of the Piedmont Post-Graduate Assembly. He helped to organize the South Carolina Obstetrical and Gynecological Society and the South Atlantic Association of Obstetrics and Gynecology. He was one of the founders of the American College of Obstetrics and Gynecology and is a diplomate of the American Board of Obstetrics and Gynecology.

In the South Carolina Medical Association he was for a long time active as chairman of the Committee on Maternal Welfare.

Dr. Guess was always interested in writing and was the author of *A Medical History of Greenville County, South Carolina.* For more than 20 years he was a member of the board of trustees of the Medical College during its most active period of expansion. He served as editor of the *Bulletin* of the Greenville County Medical Society for many years, and was on the editorial board of the *Journal of the South Carolina Medical Association.* He produced numerous writings on a variety of subjects. He was very active in the organization of the South Carolina Blue Cross and Blue Shield and was president of the board of directors of Blue Shield. He served as medical director of both organizations for some time. As a sound practitioner, author, editor, administrator, and participant in the civic and cultural life of Greenville he made a distinguished place for himself in the community and in the state.

Dr. Guess was given an honorary LL.D. degree at the College of Charleston in 1960.

SAMUEL EUGENE HARMON
1871-1935

A native of Lexington County, Dr. Harmon attended Newberry College and then proceeded to the Medical Department of the University of Nashville, where he graduated in medicine in 1899. Afterwards he spent a year at the New York Postgraduate Hospital. He was in general practice for ten years, later becoming a fellow of the American College of Surgeons and confining himself to general surgery, in which he took many postgraduate courses.

Dr. Harmon practiced in Columbia, where he was president of the local medical society and the district society. Early in his career he became much interested in organized medicine and was a militant proponent of its rights and responsibilities. In World War I he volunteered his service but was instructed to remain at home. He was surgeon for the Southern Railway in Columbia. His special interest was the Columbia Children's Clinic, which he supported vigorously. He was a councillor of the South Carolina Medical Association before election to the presidency.

JAMES ADAMS HAYNE

1872-1953

Born in Baltimore of South Carolina parentage, Dr. Hayne lived out most of his life in this state. He attended The Citadel, the

University of South Carolina, the University of Virginia, and graduated from the Medical College of the State of South Carolina in 1895. Thereafter he practiced briefly in Greenville, then in Athens, Ga., and finally in Blackstock. In Greenville he was connected with the Carolina Sanitarium. After a year in military service in the Spanish-American War he returned to Blackstock and remained there until 1904, when he became examining surgeon in the Pension Department at Washington. Later he worked in the Isthmian Canal Service in Panama and served as an Army medical officer.

In 1911 he was elected state health officer of South Carolina and served until 1944, when he assumed health educational duties with the Health Department. He was a director of the National Foundation for Infantile Paralysis and headed a state fund drive for 1948-1949. He was also a director of the National Mental Health Association. He was past president of the southern branch of the American Public Health Association and of the Conference of State and Provincial Health Authorities of North America, chairman of the Public Health Section of the Southern Medical Association, and held membership in a number of other medical organizations.

Under Dr. Hayne's administration the State Board of Health made many advances in new programs and expansion of its normal activities.

He was chairman of the Section on Preventive and Industrial Medicine and Public Health of the American Medical Association and a member of its House of Delegates, past president of the Columbia Medical Society, executive secretary of the American

Public Health Association, and professor of public health administration at the Medical College of the State of South Carolina, from
which he received the honorary degree of Doctor of Public Health
in 1926.

Dr. Hayne was a popular and jovial figure, a raconteur with a
keen memory.

ROLFE ELDRIDGE HUGHES
1868-1933

Widely known as an eminent practitioner of Laurens County who
gave the best of himself to his patients, Dr. Hughes was born in
Columbia, Va. of an old Virginia family. He was reared at his
Virginia home, where he attended Miller's School and then proceeded to the University of Maryland, where he received his medical degree in 1892. After graduation he started general practice at
Abingdon, Va., remaining there until he went to Laurens in 1898.
He held membership in numerous medical organizations and served
as secretary-treasurer for the Tri-State Association for seventeen
years, until he was made its president in 1907.

DOUGLAS JENNINGS
1894-1946

Douglas Jennings, a native of Bennettsville, came of a family which included many physicians.

He attended the College of Charleston, graduated at the Medical College of the State of South Carolina in 1919, and afterward served internships at the Roper Hospital.

Upon his return to Bennettsville he engaged in general practice for five years, later confining his work to surgery, gynecology, and obstetrics. He was responsible for establishing the Bennettsville Hospital, which opened in 1922 and preceded the first stages of the present hospital, the Marlboro County Hospital, begun in 1928 and opened in 1929.

Dr. Jennings served as president of the Tri-State Medical Association, of the Marlboro County Medical Society, and of the Pee Dee Medical Association. He was a fellow of the American College of Surgeons, and a senior fellow of the Southeastern Surgical Congress. He was for a time on the board of trustees of the Medical College of the State of South Carolina and was a member of the Council of the South Carolina Medical Association before becoming president.

Dr. Jennings wrote a number of papers on surgical subjects. He was responsible for inaugurating the annual Bennettsville Medical Meeting which has become a classic affair in the state. His many civic activities were well known.

JAMES WILKINSON JERVEY
1874-1945

A member of a distinguished and prominent family which included many physicians, Dr. Jervey was well known for his ability

in his specialty and likewise for his ready wit and skill as a speaker and raconteur. He achieved national recognition and was a constant worker for the good of the South Carolina Medical Associtaion.

Born in Charleston, he was educated in preparatory schools there and attended the University of South Carolina for two years, after which he received his medical degree from the Medical College of the State of South Carolina in 1897. He pursued postgraduate instruction at the New York Eye Infirmary and continued his search for additional knowledge abroad. In 1898 he settled in Greenville and began the practice of ophthalmology and otolaryngology. He became associated with the local railroads in a professional capacity. He was a fellow of the American College of Surgeons, and diplomate of the American Board of Ophthalmic Examinations and of the American Board of Otolaryngology. During World War I he was in the Medical Service Corps of the National Defense system.

In Greenville he established the Jervey Eye, Ear, and Throat Hospital, a private institution which continued to function until after his death. He also was very active in organizing the Greenville General Hospital. He served as president of the Greenville County Medical Society, his district and state societies and of the South Carolina Society of Ophthalmology and Otolaryngology. He was chairman of the Section of Ophthalmology and Otolaryngology and later president of the Southern Medical Association. Having served as chairman of the southern section and as a member of Council of the American Laryngological, Rhinological, and Otological Society, he was elevated to the presidency of that organization. He was also a member of the American Ophthalmological Society and of the American Bronchoscopic Society.

Dr. Jervey was of a literary turn, a voracious reader, and an excellent writer as well as an engaging speaker. He edited the *Journal of the South Carolina Medical Association* for some four years in its early days. In his latter years he agreed to conduct the *Bulletin of the Greenville County Medical Society*. He wrote many scientific papers. Dr. Jervey was one of the most prominent figures in South Carolina medicine of his day, and was listed in "Who's Who in America".

GEORGE DEAN JOHNSON
1907-

Dr. George Dean Johnson was born in Spartanburg in 1907 and obtained his A.B. degree from The Citadel in 1929. He attended

the Medical College of the State of South Carolina for two years then transferred to Jefferson Medical College, where he graduated in 1934. Thereafter, he served as intern for one year at Bryn Mawr Hospital and later held a residency in pediatrics at St. Luke's Hospital in New York. For three months he was chief resident at Seaside Hospital on Staten Island and practiced pediatrics for one year in Schenectady, New York. After this time he was instructor in pediatrics for one year at the Medical College of the State of South Carolina and then entered the practice of pediatrics in Spartanburg (1939).

Dr. Johnson is a diplomate of the American Board of Pediatrics (1941) and is a fellow of the American Academy of Pediatrics. He is past president of the Spartanburg County Medical Society and the Ninth District Medical Society, and was a delegate to the AMA from the South Carolina Medical Association for a number of years, serving as a member of the Council on Constitution and

Bylaws of the AMA. For many years he was on the board of the South Carolina Medical Care Plan and was its president for two years. He has been engaged in many community affairs as president of the Spartanburg Rotary Club, president of the Chamber of Commerce of Greater Spartanburg, member of the school board of Spartanburg District 7 for 15 years, and chairman for 13 years. He was one of the founders and one of the presidents of the South Carolina School Boards Association. In 1955 he was given the Service to Mankind Award by District 8 of Sertoma International.

Dr. Johnson has long been efficiently active in the affairs of the South Carolina Medical Association, and achieved its presidency in 1967. He has also been president of the South Carolina Pediatric Society.

KENNETH MERRILL LYNCH
1887-

Kenneth Merrill Lynch was born November 27, 1887 in Hamilton County, Texas. His entire youth was spent in an environment just

emerging from frontier conditions. After graduating at the University of Texas in 1910 with the M.D. degree and with honors leading to both Phi Beta Kappa and Alpha Omega Alpha, he engaged in general practice at Rule, Texas, for several months while awaiting an appointment as resident in pathology at the Philadelphia General Hospital, December 1910. There he wrote his autopsy reports, in longhand, in the same large ledger-like book as William Osler had written his. There he initiated the first routine microscopic examinations ever done at that hospital, in the course of which he uncovered an undiagnosed cancer of the lung, beginning a research interest that has continued all his life.

After a year as resident in pathology, Dr. Lynch was appointed instructor in gross morbid anatomy at the School of Medicine of the University of Pennsylvania, under Professor Allen J. Smith, where he continued until he accepted the professorship of pathology at the Medical College of the State of South Carolina, and at the age of 26 became the first full-time member of the faculty of that institution. He has recorded that experience in some detail in an article entitled "The Development of Pathology in South Carolina."[1] From a beginning, as simply one man located in an unequipped barn-like room, the new department progressed to become consistently accepted nationally as the main pillar on which the school stood, with the practically routine expression in accreditation surveys and reports as "doing an impossible job."

Following World War I, in which he served briefly as a captain, M. C., U. S. Army, economic conditions brought additional difficulties, and he reluctantly gave up his position in South Carolina and engaged in private practice in Dallas from July 1921 to December 1926. Then he returned to the Medical College faculty post on a "geographic" full-time basis, i.e., with the privilege of consultation practice in pathology, but only within the institution. In that combined teaching and service capacity he remained until retirement to emeritus status July 1, 1960.

A natural urge toward the third function of medical education, research, stimulated at Pennsylvania by Dr. Allen J. Smith, led to experimentation in the transmissibility of Lepra bacilli by the common bed bug, and to studies of protozoa parasitic in man. His studies in the latter subject, in which he was the first to report in vitro cultivation of parasitic flagellates, *Trichomonas sp.*, were continued in South Carolina, and his publications, including a book titled *Protozoan Parasitism of the Alimentary Tract*[2] brought a world-wide acquaintance and led to the presidency of the American Society of Tropical Medicine (1930). They were the basis of the award of the Research Medal of the Southern Medical Association (1921), honorable mention in the exhibits of the American Medical Association (1923), and the honorary degree of LL.D. by the University of South Carolina (1930).

Connected with these and other researches and publications of that time, as well as the development of his Department of Pathology, Dr. Lynch was invited to co-authorship with Professor H. W. C. Vines, M.D., of the Charing Cross Hospital, London, in the Fifteenth Revised Edition of *Green's Manual of Pathology*.[3]

In that period he also became a founder of the American Society of Clinical Pathologists (1923) and president in 1930, chairman of the Section on Pathology of both the American Medical Association (1924) and the Southern Medical Association (1925), president of the South Carolina Medical Association (1930-1931), vice-president of the American Medical Association (1935), member of the board of governors of the American College of Physicians (1925-1927) and (1936-1943), chairman of the S. C. Cancer Commission (1939-1944), member of the South Carolina State Board of Health (1935-1945) and chairman (1940-1944), as well as serving in various other capacities in professional organizations.

Although Dr. Lynch's researches and publications have covered a wide range (his bibliography contains more than 118 articles and three books), there are two other particular fields of accomplishment and wide interest besides his work in parasitology. Coincidentally with other researchers, but independently, he identified as granuloma inguinale a disease which had frustrated the staffs of hospitals of this country for many years. In one of the earliest ventures in chemotherapy he was given charge of a group of these hopeless patients in the Roper Hospital, and made and gave antimony solutions for injections that produced a spectacular cure. In the 1921 Scientific Exhibits of the American Medical Association, he was awarded the Gold Medal for his demonstration of the disease and its cure.

Then in the 1930's, and continuing to the present, Dr. Lynch became interested in the industrial dust diseases of the lungs. His studies and publications, along with those of other investigators in the United States and abroad, have revolutionized protective measures for the workers in the asbestos industry from the mine to the factory, and have likewise affected other dusty trades. With the collaboration of Dr. W. Atmar Smith of the clinical faculty, whose patients provided the opportunity, Dr. Lynch is credited with the first report (1935) of the association of cancer of the lung with the disease asbestosis, a problem still the subject of much concern. He also was the first to publish a complete description of the kindred disease of the lungs; kaolinosis, in kaolin workers.[4]

In 1935 he was appointed vice dean of the Medical College of the State of South Carolina, and at the end of 1943 he was elected dean. He immediately launched already prepared plans for the development of a complete "Health and Medical Educational Service and Research Center" of university type, with the Medical College as the "hub".

In recognition of his efforts the College of Charleston conferred upon him the degree of LL.D. in 1945, and Clemson University the honorary degree of Sc.D. in 1954, while the Southern Medical Association awarded him its Distinguished Service Medal in 1957, and the University of Texas conferred its Ashbel Smith Medallion Award for Service to Medicine in 1967.

From the position of president and dean of the faculty, Dr. Lynch retired July 1, 1960, with the title of chancellor. He remains busy with his continued researches, world-wide correspondence, and the evaluation of research grant applications of others, having served on an advisory council of the National Institutes of Health and the Scientific Advisory Board (of which he remains chairman) of the Council for Tobacco Research—U. S. A., a foundation or endowment type of organization.

In 1970 he published *Medical Schooling in South Carolina,* incorporating and revising articles published in the *Journal of the South Carolina Medical Association* from 1962-1968.

REFERENCES

1. *J. S. Carolina Med. Ass.,* 61:190-194 (July 1965).
2. The Macmillan Co., N. Y., 1930.
3. Bailliere, Tindall, and Cox, London, and Wm. Wood & Co., Baltimore, 1934.
4. K. M. Lynch, M.D. and Forde A. McIver, M.D., "Pneumoconiosis from Exposure to Kaolin Dust: Kaolinosis." *Amer. J. Path.,* 30:1117 (Nov.-Dec. 1954).

JAMES HIGGINS McINTOSH
1866-1944

A native of Newberry, Dr. McIntosh received his A.B. degree at Newberry College in 1884, then attended Johns Hopkins University for two years, later transferring to the College of Physicians and Surgeons in New York, and graduating there in 1888. He then pursued postgraduate experience in Bellevue Hospital and The Lying-In Hospital before turning to a general practice in Newberry. After ten years he moved to Columbia where he spent the rest of his life.

In Columbia he was chief of staff at the Baptist Hospital, president of the Columbia Medical Society, of the Seventh District Society, and of the Tri-State Medical Association. He was a member of the Association of Surgeons of the Atlantic Coast Line and gave service to his local draft board. The Columbia Medical Society arranged a testimonial dinner in which gifts of a silver pitcher and goblets were made. His portrait hangs in the Columbia Hospital.

Dr. McIntosh was highly esteemed as a courteous and ethical practitioner. He wrote a number of papers and addresses, chiefly for the South Carolina Medical Association, which he at one time served as vice-president.

FRANK HILTON McLEOD
1868-1944

Born in Richmond County, N. C., Dr. McLeod attended Wofford College and the Medical Department of the University of Nashville,

where he graduated in medicine in 1888. After two years of training he located in Florence and began working as a general practitioner. Later he specialized in surgery. In 1906 he established the Florence Infirmary and Training School, a small project in a seven-room house on West Cheves Street, which grew into the large McLeod Infirmary. He was largely instrumental also in the establishment of the Florence-Darlington Tuberculosis Sanatorium.

Dr. McLeod was a pioneer in surgery in his area and achieved an enviable reputation. He was one of the founders of the American College of Surgeons, president of the Tri-State Medical Association, councillor for the Southern Medical Association, a regent of the South Carolina State Hospital, and founder of the McLeod Infirmary. He received the Sullivan Award from the University of South Carolina in 1928 and an honorary LL.D. from the same institution in 1935. He was awarded the American Legion plaque for outstanding service in 1941 and upon his 70th birthday he was the honored guest at a testimonial dinner attended by prominent people from all over the state.

Dr. McLeod was known for his energy, enthusiasm, integrity, and earnestness, and his devotion to his patients. His bust is to be seen in the McLeod Infirmary. He was a man who participated vigorously in civic and religious activities and was well known as the first citizen of the Pee Dee area.

JAMES CARLISLE McLEOD
1897-1947

James McLeod, son of the well known surgeon Frank H. McLeod, who was also a president of the South Carolina Medical Association,

was born in Florence. He attended local schools and studied at Davidson College briefly, but removed to the University of North Carolina, where he obtained his degree of A.B. in 1917. He then began his medical training at Harvard Medical School, transferred to Cornell University Medical College and graduated in 1922, thereafter serving two years on a surgical service at Bellevue Hospital. After his return to Florence he became superintendent of the McLeod Infirmary, and was its chief surgeon after the retirement of his father.

During World War I he enlisted but saw no active service. In the second World War he headed the District Advisory Board for a time and then received a commission as a major in the Medical Corps. While preparing for overseas duty he sustained a back injury which prevented him from going abroad.

Dr. McLeod followed in his father's footsteps to eminence in surgery. He was a member of the American College of Surgeons and the International College of Surgeons. His civic and social connections were very numerous. He was considered as a most prominent citizen of his area.

In 1946 he entered the gubernatorial race and made an excellent showing in his first political offering. It was thought that he would undoubtedly pursue a political career, while continuing his medical activities, but this trend was cut short by his premature death.

Dr. McLeod was interested in organized medicine from the time he returned to South Carolina. He became president of his county and district societies and served as councillor from the Sixth District before achieving the presidency of the SCMA. He was a leader in the activities of the Committee of Seventeen which had much to do with promoting the expansion of the Medical College.

Dr. McLeod was known and respected over the whole state. He died of coronary thrombosis at the age of 50.

RODERICK MACDONALD
1898-

Roderick Macdonald was born in Blackstock, S. C. and took his preliminary education there. After serving in World War I as a

second lieutenant in the infantry, he completed his academic career by graduating from the University of South Carolina in 1919. He received his M.D. degree from the Medical College of the State of South Carolina in 1923. After completion of an internship at Roper Hospital and a year as health officer of Fairfield County, he began his training in ophthalmology and otolaryngology at the Jefferson Medical College Hospital in Philadelphia. Later he was associated for a short time with Dr. Josiah E. Smith of Charleston in the private practice of his specialty.

Dr. Macdonald moved to Columbia in 1927 and organized the eye, ear, nose, and throat department of the South Carolina State Hospital. He settled in Rock Hill in 1934 and became associated with Dr. W. B. Ward at the Fennell Infirmary for several months before entering into his own private practice. He became a diplomate of the American Board of Otolaryngology in 1939 and of the American Board of Ophthalmology in 1942.

Dr. Macdonald has always been vitally interested in continuing his studies with short postgraduate courses and in the advancement of organized medicine in his state. His pursuit of knowledge in his specialty has taken him to many medical centers here and abroad, including Vienna, Budapest, London, and Glasgow. He has studied at George Washington University, Harvard, the Universities of Pennsylvania, Virginia, and Indiana, and the New York Ear and Eye Infirmary. He served a year's residency (1941-1942) at the New Haven Hospital and was assistant in the Department of Ophthalmology at the Yale University School of Medicine.

He has served as president of the York County Medical Society and of the Fifth District Medical Society, and had a long tenure as a member of the Council of the South Carolina Medical Association. He is at present a member of the South Carolina Board of Medical Examiners, having served formerly as its chairman. Membership in the societies of his specialty include the South Carolina Society of Ophthalmology and Otolaryngology, the American Academy of Ophthalmology and Otolaryngology, the American College of Surgeons, of which he has been governor representing South Carolina, the International College of Surgeons, and the American Laryngological, Rhinological, and Otological Society. He is also a member of the Association of Surgeons of the Southern Railway System. He has been chief of staff of St. Phillip's Hospital in Rock Hill and the York County Hospital and a member of the board of trustees of the latter institution.

LELAND OSGOOD MAULDIN

1878-1932

A native of Pickens, Dr. Mauldin attended Clemson College where he received the degree of B.S. in 1900. His medical degree was attained at the Medical College of the State of South Carolina in 1903.

After graduation he did some general practice for a short time, and spent a brief period in the civil service with the Bureau of Pensions. Postgraduate courses in Europe were followed by his specialization in diseases of the eye, ear, nose, and throat in Greenville.

He was president of the Tri-State Medical Association, a member of the American Academy of Ophthalmology and Otolaryngology, and a fellow of the American College of Surgeons. He published a number of papers. During World War I he was president of the Medical Advisory Board for the First District. He served also as councillor for the Fourth District of the South Carolina Medical Association and was chairman in 1920. He also held the presidency of the Greenville County Medical Society and of the staff of the Greenville General Hospital. A tablet in the latter commemorates his memory.

CHARLES RAYSOR MAY
1872-1947

Charles May was born at Yorkville. His father was a physician and surgeon. Dr. May attended the Medical College of Virginia in Richmond and graduated from the Medical College of the State of South Carolina in 1897. He practiced for a time at Blenheim and later settled permanently at Bennettsville. He then pursued his interests in surgery at the New York Postgraduate Medical School, and devoted much of his practice to this branch of medicine.

Dr. May served as president of the Marlboro County Medical Society and of the Pee Dee Medical Association. For many years he was also councillor for the Sixth District of the South Carolina Medical Association. At one time he was vice-president of the Tri-State Medical Association. He engaged in many social, business, and professional activities and was a well known and highly esteemed personality of his area.

ORLANDO BENEDICT MAYER, III
1897-

The son of Dr. O. B. Mayer, II, he was born in Newberry and received his primary schooling there, later graduating from New-

berry College (A.B.) in 1917. He then entered the Medical College of the State of South Carolina and completed two years, transferring to Western Reserve University School of Medicine and receiving his degree in 1921. Internship and residency at Lakeside Hospital, Cleveland, followed and in 1924 he received the degree of M.A. in medicine from Western Reserve University. He then went to Columbia, where he practiced internal medicine, later pursuing medical studies with courses in Vienna, London, and other European cities.

He is a diplomate of the American Board of Internal Medicine, and a member of the American College of Physicians. He was at one time a medical consultant at the Army hospital at Fort Jackson.

In 1941 he entered military service, becoming Chief of Medicine at Station Hospital, Fort Jackson, and later was transferred to Barnes General Hospital, Vancouver, Wash., as chief of medicine, achieving the rank of colonel. He then resumed his private practice in Columbia.

He has been president of the Columbia Medical Society and the Columbia Medical Club. As councillor for the Second District he served the South Carolina Medical Association well, becoming chairman of its Council in 1947 and holding the office for seven years before election to the presidency.

BENJAMIN NEELY MILLER
1910-

Born in Smyrna in York County and afterwards living in Hickory Grove, Dr. Miller attended the public schools of the latter and

graduated in 1928. He then entered Duke University where he received the degree of B.S. in medicine in 1931 and his M.D. degree in 1935. He served a clinical residency at Duke University Hospital from 1935 to 1937 and for a year afterward was an instructor at the University of Alabama Medical School, after which time he entered the private practice of internal medicine in Columbia.

Dr. Miller is a member of many organizations. He is a fellow and life member of the American College of Physicians, fellow of the American College of Allergists, fellow of the American Academy of Allergy, and is certified by the American Board of Internal Medicine (1948). He was president of the South Carolina Society of Internal Medicine (1957-1959), president of the Columbia Medical Society (1957), chief of staff of Providence, Baptist, and Columbia hospitals at various times, and president of the Southeastern Allergy Association (1955-1956). He is medical consultant for the South Carolina State Hospital, the State Department of Vocational Rehabilitation, and the Shaw Air Force Base Hospital (1952 to date). For a time, he was medical consultant for the Veteran's Administration. He has served as a member of the board of trustees of Duke University and was president of the Duke Alumni Association in 1961 and also president of the Duke Medical Alumni Association from 1955 to 1961.

He is a member of a number of civic and social clubs, of United Community Services, and of the Medical Advisory Committee of the United Health and Medical Research Foundation of South Carolina, and has important business connections.

Dr. Miller, long active in organized medicine, served as secretary of the Association from 1963 to 1968.

CHARLES ARDEN MOBLEY

1888-

Born in Rock Hill, Dr. Mobley received his early education there, then attended the University of Tennessee and completed his medi-

cal course at the Medical College of the State of South Carolina in 1910. He practiced briefly at Van Wyck in Lancaster County before going to Rock Hill, where he was associated with Dr. W. W. Fennell and specialized in urology. Later he moved to Orangeburg, where he established the Orangeburg Hospital (later called the Tri-County Hospital), now the Orangeburg Regional Hospital. At that time it was a small institution of 25 beds. He became its chief surgeon and continued to hold this position until his retirement in 1948.

He was a member of the founders group and a fellow of the American College of Surgeons, which he joined in 1919, and was a member of the founders group of the American Board of Surgery in 1937. During World War I he served as a member of the Advisory Medical Board in Greenville.

GOTTLOB AUGUSTUS NEUFFER
1861-1935

Born in Orangeburg of German parentage, he was reared in Charleston, where he studied as an assistant to a pharmacist and attained sufficient knowledge to pass the requirements for a license in 1879. Later he attended the Medical College of the State of South Carolina, where he graduated in 1884. He then served as house surgeon at City Hospital in Charleston. He eventually settled at Abbeville, where he conducted a general practice, from which he took time in 1901 for work at the New York Polyclinic Medical School and Hospital.

Dr. Neuffer was a trustee of the Medical College and a councillor for the Third District of the Medical Association and chairman of Council at one time. He was much interested in public affairs, was president of his county and district societies and of the Association of Seaboard Airline Railway Surgeons. He was also vice-president of the Tri-State Medical Association and was appointed surgeon general of the South Carolina Militia. His practice spanned a course of 50 years. He was known as a kindly, friendly, and efficient physician.

FRANK CAPERS OWENS
1898-

Dr. Owens was born in Richland County, attended the Columbia city schools, and graduated from the University of South Carolina with a B.S. degree in 1919. He

then entered the Medical College of the State of South Carolina, where he became a doctor of medicine in 1923. He served as intern at the South Carolina Baptist Hospital, then began the practice of medicine in Columbia.

In 1942 he entered the Medical Corps of the Air Force as captain, and was discharged 3½ years later as a lieutenant colonel. He was elected mayor of Columbia upon his return and served four years (1946-1950).

Dr. Owens has functioned in the capacity of president of the Lions Club, as state chairman of the National Foundation for Infantile Paralysis, and as state chairman of the Heart Association Drive. While mayor, he was president of the South Carolina Municipal Association, and a member of its national board of directors. Dr. Owens served as president of the Columbia Medical Society, and as president of the Columbia Art Association. Dr. Owens was twice delegate to the National Democratic Convention, served as president of the South Carolina Industrial Medical Society, and was president of the A. C. Moore Parent Teachers Association. He was appointed state chairman of the Medical Advisory Committee to Selective Service, and served in that capacity from its inception. He was at one time chairman of the Committee on Legislation and Public Policy of the South Carolina Medical Association and a member of the South Carolina Board of Health. He is a member of the South Carolina Water Pollution Board. He is a former president of the Columbia Medical Club, a member of the National Association of Food Research, and a member of the Forum Club. Dr. Owens is a Shriner, a Mason, an

Elk, and is a member of the American Legion and of the 40 and 8. He is a member of the staff of the Columbia, Providence, and South Carolina Baptist hospitals and a member of the Medical Board of the South Carolina Retirement System.

Dr. Owens has always had an interest in political matters and served the South Carolina Medical Association more than faithfully in influencing legislation. In 1969 he was elected State Senator from Richland County.

EDWARD FROST PARKER
1867-1938

Dr. Parker was the son of Dr. Francis LeJau Parker and came of a distinguished Charleston family. After attending schools in

Charleston he went to the South Carolina Military Academy, then proceeded to the University of Virginia, where he was enrolled in modern language and historical science for the year 1886-1887. Graduation at the Medical College of the State of South Carolina followed in 1889. Here he achieved high scholastic honors.

After a year as house officer in the City Hospital, he entered into general practice, but soon pursued postgraduate courses in Baltimore and London in the diseases of the eye, ear, nose, and throat. In 1895 he confined his practice to these diseases and achieved eminence in his specialty. He was a member of the American Laryngological, Rhinological, and Otological Society, and was certified by the American Board of Ophthalmic Examinations and the American Board of Otolaryngology.

Like his father before him, Dr. Parker became associated early in his career with the Medical College of the State of South Carolina and held various positions in the departments of physiology, anatomy, and medical jurisprudence, finally becoming professor of ophthalmology and otology and executive head of the department of the diseases of the eye, ear, nose, and throat at the college. He held the title of dean from 1906-1908, which position he resigned because of press of other duties.

During his career he wrote many articles, among them the "History of Surgery in South Carolina". He was an honorary fellow of the American Laryngological, Rhinological, and Otological Society, and a fellow of the American College of Surgeons. In the Medical Society of South Carolina (Charleston) he was always active and achieved the presidency after serving on many active boards of the society. His portrait was commissioned by the Medical Society and hangs in the Roper Hospital.

Dr. Parker was oculist for the Southern Railway Company for many years and served on the local medical advisory board during World War I. He was blessed with a great deal of personality and humor, and was one who had high respect for the ethics of medicine and honest dealings with his fellow man. He was a genial host and was always good company, a very popular member of his profession in Charleston and elsewhere.

WILLIAM LOUIS PERRY
1912-

A native of Chesterfield, William L. Perry graduated B.S. from Wake Forest College and received his M.D. degree from the Med-

ical College of the State of South Carolina in 1938. He served his internship at McLeod Infirmary in Florence and has been in private practice in Chesterfield since 1940.

Dr. Perry has been chairman of the Chesterfield County Board of Education for ten years, is a past president of Chesterfield County Medical Society and of the Pee Dee Medical Association. He is a member of the American Academy of General Practice.

Dr. Perry was a councillor of the Sixth Medical District for nine years and completed his term as chairman of council before his election to the presidency.

Dr. Perry has participated in many community activities. He has been interested in Masonry and received the Silver Beaver award for his work with the Boy Scouts of his area.

THOMAS ANTLEY PITTS
1893-

Thomas Pitts, the son of a physician, was born in Saluda County. He attended Newberry College for two years and then entered the

Medical College of the State of South Carolina by special certificate, graduating in 1916. He became instructor in physiology and later in pathology, and served on the house staff of Roper Hospital. In World War I he saw service as a captain in the Medical Corps of the British Army.

Returning to Saluda, he entered general practice with his father for a short time, afterwards serving as assistant superintendent of the Louisiana State Charity Hospital in Shreveport, where he developed his interest in radiology. Graduate work in that branch of medicine prepared him for his position as director of laboratories in the South Carolina Baptist Hospital in Columbia. He has been associated with that hospital and the other hospitals of the area since 1923.

Dr. Pitts is a member of the American Radiological Society, a diplomate of the American Board of Radiology, a fellow of the American College of Physicians, and consultant to the Columbia hospitals. He served as president of the Columbia Medical Society, the Second District Medical Association, and was long a member and finally chairman of the Council of the South Carolina Medical Association. He was also for some years a delegate to the American Medical Association from that body. He periodically visited a number of centers for refreshment of his knowledge of radiology. He also conducted research studies in cancer at the Baptist Hospital.

Dr. Pitts has an abiding and active interest in the affairs of the Medical College. He was a trustee, and after 1941 was chairman of the board for a total of 38 years of service. During this time he was most active in promoting the welfare of the institution and worked closely with Dr. Lynch in his efforts to bring about an expansion of the college. The Alumni Association took cognizance of his work by presenting him with a testimonial silver tray, and the trustees and friends of the Medical College had his portrait painted for the Medical College Hospital.

Dr. Pitts has always been active in the affairs of the Columbia Medical Society. When *The Recorder* was established he acted as the first editor.

EBENEZER WIDEMAN PRESSLY
1863-1931

Dr. Pressly was born in Anderson County and lived at Due West, where he graduated from Erskine College in 1883. He then

proceeded to the University of Maryland and received his medical degree in 1887, along with a gold medal for his academic achievements. After graduation he practiced at Clover for a while, later removing to Greenville, and finally returning to Clover in his latter years.

He was a member of his local Draft Exemption Board in World War I and volunteered for service in the Army Medical Corps, progressing from first lieutenant to lieutenant colonel, later becoming the commanding officer of the Army hospital at Camp Sevier. For some time, he was also a member of the State Board of Medical Examiners.

Dr. Pressly had a reputation as a lovable character of unusual intellectual attainments. He was known in the South Carolina Medical Association as a brilliant speaker.

WILLIAM LOWRY PRESSLY
1887-1954

Dr. "Buck" Pressly was born and lived out his life in Due West, where he received his early education before attending and finishing Erskine College, at which he achieved the A.B. degree in 1908. He then entered the Atlanta Medical College (now Emory University School of Medicine) and graduated in 1912. Thereafter he pursued hospital experience for three years at Jefferson Hospital in Roanoke, Va. During the summers of 1912-1914 he engaged in local professional baseball, in which he achieved quite a reputation.

Returning to his home on January 1, 1916, Dr. Pressly entered general practice as a "horse and buggy doctor" and followed this profession vigorously until the time of his death. During his career he served as a captain in the Army (1917-1918), stimulated local immunization clinics throughout his area, especially against typhoid fever, and sponsored at his own expense a number of lectures by outstanding physicians. He was largely instrumental in promoting the construction of the Abbeville Hospital and its later additions.

For many years he served as physician at Erskine College. He was always a tireless worker, ready to promote any good cause, widely respected and beloved. He was president of his county medical society in 1920, president of the Third District Medical Society, vice-president of the Tri-State Medical Association (1926), and served on the Council on Medical Education and Hospitals and was chairman of the Medical Preparedness Committee (1939-1940) of the American Medical Association. He was chairman of the section on general practice of the Southern Medical Association for two terms and chairman of Council of this organization. He was active in the South Carolina Chapter of the Academy of General Practice and became its chairman.

During World War II he did valiant service as chairman of the Appeal Board for Selective Service. For some years he was a member of the Executive Committee of the State Board of Health. In 1948 he acquired a great distinction in receiving the National General Practitioners Award of the American Medical Association.

As a true rural doctor in a town of 700 people he was interested in farming activities in his county. After seven years as a member he became chairman of the Council of the South Carolina Medical Association (1932-1940). A plaque erected posthumously at the Medical College (1956) by the South Carolina Medical Association reads:

IN MEMORIAM

WILLIAM LOWRY PRESSLY, M.D., D.P.H.
1887 - 1954

PHYSICIAN AND CITIZEN EXTRAORDINARY

EXECUTIVE COMMITTEE, SOUTH CAROLINA
STATE BOARD OF HEALTH—1941 - 1954

PRESIDENT, SOUTH CAROLINA MEDICAL ASSOCIATION
1941

CHAIRMAN, PROCUREMENT AND ASSIGNMENT
SERVICE FOR SOUTH CAROLINA—WORLD WAR II

DOCTOR OF THE YEAR
AMERICAN MEDICAL ASSOCIATION—1948

COUNCIL ON MEDICAL EDUCATION AND HOSPITALS
AMERICAN MEDICAL ASSOCIATION—1948 - 1954

PRESENTED BY THE

SOUTH CAROLINA MEDICAL ASSOCIATION, 1956

Another testimonial plaque was placed on his office by his community. In 1948 Erskine conferred on him the degree of LL.D. In 1949 he received the honorary degree of Doctor of Public Health at the Medical College of South Carolina.

Dr. Pressly was a fine example of the general practitioner with broad professional and humanitarian interests, an outstanding physician of his generation in South Carolina.

JULIAN PLEASANTS PRICE
1901-

Dr. Price was born in Sinchang, China, October 22, 1901. He received his A.B. and M.A. degrees at Davidson College and his

M.D. degree at Johns Hopkins in 1926. After hospital experience in Baltimore and New York City, he came to Florence to start the practice of pediatrics in 1928. He soon became interested in the activities of the South Carolina Medical Association and was elected to the multiple position of secretary-treasurer-editor in 1940-1950. Some years later he served as president 1965-1966. From 1941-1953 he edited the *Journal of the South Carolina Medical Association.*

Dr. Price's activities have been numerous, notable, and productive. One of his early accomplishments was the writing of a book, *The Young Doctor Who Thinks Out Loud* (1931).

Among the responsible positions held by Dr. Price were: chairman of the Joint Commission on the Accreditation of Hospitals, member of the board of directors of the American Medical Educational Foundation, dean of the Southern Pediatric Seminar at Saluda, N. C., member of the House of Delegates of the AMA for four years, member of the Legislative Committee of the AMA, member of the Advisory Committee to the State Medical Journal Advertising Bureau, past president of the Conference of Presidents and other officers of State Medical Associations, member of the board of trustees of the American Medical Association.

Dr. Price has also served as medical director of the South Carolina Home for Convalescent Children in Florence. He is a diplomate of the American Board of Pediatrics and a member of the American Academy of Pediatrics, as well as of numerous other medical organizations. He has enjoyed an enviable reputation for his work with charitable and educational institutions.

WILLIAM HUTSON PRIOLEAU
1897-

Dr. Prioleau was born in Summerville, son of Dr. and Mrs. William H. Prioleau. He attended Woodberry Forest School, Orange, Va., 1913-1916. He received his B.S. degree from the University of South Carolina in 1918, and his M.D. degree from Johns Hopkins Medical School in 1923. The following year he served an internship at Johns Hopkins Hospital, and from 1924 to 1928 he served as fellow and resident in surgery at the Cleveland Clinic, Cleveland, Ohio. He was licensed to practice in South Carolina in 1929, and has been engaged in the private practice of general surgery in Charleston since that date. He advanced through the various grades to become clinical professor of surgery at the Medical University of South Carolina and has served as chairman of the surgical division of Roper Hospital.

His special examinations include the National Board of Medical Examiners, 1924, and the American Board of Surgery, Founders Group, 1937. He was a member of the Board of Commissioners, Roper Hospital, and a member of the Charleston County Board of Health.

Dr. Prioleau is a fellow of the American College of Surgeons and a past president of its South Carolina Chapter, a past president of the South Carolina Surgical Society, of the Association of Surgeons of the Southern Railway Company, of the Southern Surgeons Club, and the Medical Society of South Carolina, and a fellow of the Southern Surgical Association.

He is the author of many articles in general and special medical journals and in the lay press.

CHARLES MAYRANT REES
1862-1913

Born in Stateburg, Dr. Rees took his preliminary education in Charleston, and graduated as a pharmacist at the Medical College

there in 1883. He then pursued the course toward a medical degree, which he achieved in 1887, serving during that interval as druggist to the City Hospital in Charleston, and remaining there as house physician until 1889.

Beside a very active practice, Dr. Rees had many teaching responsibilities. He taught in the Summer Medical School, gave courses in obstetrics and surgery at the City Hospital, and was gynecologist to the Shirras Dispensary. He also participated in the activities of the Roper Hospital Polyclinic, where he taught gynecology and abdominal surgery. Eventually he became professor of surgery in the Medical College. He was a charter member of the American College of Surgeons.

Dr. Rees was deeply interested in organized medicine and served as president of the Medical Society of South Carolina and also as a member of the Executive Committee of the State Board of Health. He belonged to many medical organizations, including the American Association of Obstetricians and Gynecologists, and contributed papers to this and other societies.

HARRY LEE SHAW
1865-1939

A native of Sumter County, Dr. Shaw studied medicine under Dr. S. C. Baker of Sumter, afterwards attended Davidson College, then the University of Virginia School of Medicine and finally receiving his degree from the Medical College of the State of South Carolina in 1891. After graduation he studied at the Post-graduate Medical School in New York.

Dr. Shaw practiced at Rodman in Chester County for a time, later in Fountain Inn, and finally in Sumter, where he was president of the Sumter County Medical Society. He also served on the State Board of Medical Examiners for many years, and entered into many civic activities.

In 1918 he entered the Medical Corps of the Army as a captain and served at Camp Jackson.

MANNING SIMONS
1846-1911

A native of Charleston, Dr. Simons graduated from the College of Charleston and from the Medical College of the State of South

Carolina, receiving his degree from the latter in 1868 and then beginning his practice. Before his academic career he had enlisted in the Confederate Army at the age of fifteen and had served as a courier for Gen. William J. Hardee.

With his associate, Dr. R. A. Kinloch, he carried on a very active medical and surgical career. He served as a volunteer during the yellow fever epidemic in Beaufort in 1877. He was interested in the St. Francis Infirmary from the time of its opening in 1882 and helped to organize its Training School for Nurses. Later he was professor of gynecology and obstetrics at the Medical College, president of the Southern Surgical and Gynecological Association, and worked actively in promoting the control of tuberculosis. He contributed many case reports to the literature and wrote an article on "Climatology and Epidemics of South Carolina" for the *Transactions of the American Medical Association*.[1]

Dr. Simons received from the College of Charleston an honorary degree of A.B. and later the degree of LL.D. He enjoyed the reputation of being one of the finest surgeons of the South, a dedicated, kindly, vocal, and dignified man.

There is a portrait of Dr. Simons in the Medical Society room at the Roper Hospital and another in the Waring Historical Library at the Medical University.

REFERENCE

1. *Trans. A.M.A.*, 23:290 (1872).

DANIEL LESESNE SMITH
1877-1947

Dr. Smith was a man of dynamic and engaging personality who pursued with vigor and success his various interests in the field of medical service and education.

He was distinguished among the few physicians of the state who specialized early in pediatrics, in which field he became nationally known and respected.

With the help of the family and through his own hard efforts Dr. Smith obtained his education at a period which offered many difficulties. After preliminary schooling in Charleston (he was a native of Berkeley County) he received his A.B. degree from Clemson in 1901 and his M.D. degree from the Medical College of the State of South Carolina in 1903. He began a very exacting general practice at Newry, S. C. and later at Great Falls, S. C. After six years of onerous medical labor he removed to Spartanburg, where he soon felt the need for a specialist in pediatrics. In 1914 he confined his work to this branch of medicine. He became vitally concerned with the development of the Spartanburg Baby Hospital, a charitable institution which was placed just across the North Carolina line at Saluda, and at the same time began to develop his own private Infants and Children's Sanatorium at the same place. Out of these grew the Southern Pediatric Seminar, a unique postgraduate educational facility which ran from 1920 until 1958 when the extensive development of postgraduate educational opportunities made it seem unnecessary. At the urging of Dr. Smith, most of the leading pediatricians of the southern states participated voluntarily in the activities of this institution and served as teachers to a group of general practitioners which grew rapidly to as many as 200 at a session. Dr. Smith's enthusiasm for spreading the gospel of good pediatrics to the general practitioner was most infectious and effective. In furthering this effort he had the particular assistance of Dr. Frank Howard Richardson, as well as numerous pediatricians who came year after year to help with the project.

Dr. Smith's other chief enthusiasm was for the Medical College, for which he worked hard and long to obtain funds to improve its status. He was responsible for inaugurating the postgraduate seminar and obtained funds for construction of the outpatient clinic and the dormitory. A bronze plaque in the dormitory bears witness to his services. Another plaque received from the faculty of the Southern Pediatric Seminar also adds evidence of the general esteem in which he was held.

Dr. Smith was a charter member of the American Academy of Pediatrics, served as chairman of the section on pediatrics of the Southern Medical Association, was president of the Spartanburg County Medical Society, a member of the State Board of Health, and visiting physician to the Cedar Springs Institute.

Dr. Smith has been characterized as a "master of the art of living. He knew how to play and when to stop, how to make new friends and how to keep them." In all of his vigorous activities he managed to keep himself in the background, from which he directed the activities of his many friendly associates.

DANIEL LESESNE SMITH, JR.

1905-

Lesesne Smith, Jr. was born in Newry, S. C., attended The Citadel, where he graduated in 1927 as B.S. before proceeding to

the Medical College of the State of South Carolina to receive his medical degree in 1931. He served his internship at Duval County Hospital in Jacksonville, Fla. and his residency at the Children's Hospital and Cincinnati General Hospital in Cincinnati, Ohio. While at the latter he received a M.S. degree from the University of Cincinnati.

Dr. Smith was associated with his father for many years in the conduct of the Southern Pediatric Seminar at Saluda. He acted as registrar and program chairman for more than ten years and was an active member of the faculty. He has practiced pediatrics in Spartanburg for most of his life and was associated professionally with his father. In 1942 he entered the Medical Corps of the Army and saw four years of active duty in New Guinea, the Philippines, and elsewhere, being separated from the service with the rank of major.

Dr. Smith is intensely interested in the activities of organized medicine. He served as chief of staff at the Spartanburg General Hospital, twice as president of the Spartanburg County Medical Society, and as president of the South Carolina Pediatric Society, the Ninth District Medical Society, and the Alumni Association of the Medical College of South Carolina. For nine years he served as a member of the Council of the South Carolina Medical Association. His civic activities have been numerous.

Dr. Smith is a fellow of the American Academy of Pediatrics and a licentiate of the American Board of Pediatrics.

WILLIAM ATMAR SMITH
1886-1971

Summerville was the place of Dr. Smith's birth and Charleston was the scene of his life. His many accomplishments in medicine,

especially in the field of chest diseases, made him an outstanding, valuable member of his community and state. A graduate of the South Carolina Military Academy, where he was prominent in football prowess, he received his B.S. degree there in 1906. Fifty years later he was to receive an honorary degree of LL.D. from his alma mater. In 1910 he graduated from the Medical College of the State of South Carolina, thereafter serving an internship at the Roper Hospital and beginning his practice. In 1916 he entered the Army as a first lieutenant and in May 1917 went overseas as a captain in the Medical Corps with the 309th Infantry, seeing much active service on the front.

The list of his connections and attainments is indeed long. He early became associated with the Medical College as a teacher and progressed through the academic grades to the final status of professor emeritus of clinical medicine. He was intensely interested in teaching, and vitally concerned with the problem of tuberculosis. He was associated with Roper Hospital and the other hospitals of the city and served as medical director of Pinehaven tuberculosis hospital for many years, seeing it through its early stages and building it steadily into an effective institution. He was chairman of the Charleston Board of Health and president of the Medical Society of South Carolina, for which he had labored long as secretary. He was a member of the American Clinical and Climatological Association as well as of numerous other medical organizations. He served on the executive committee and the board of directors of the National Tuberculosis Association and was its vice-president in 1942. He was also chairman of the medical committee of the South

Carolina Tuberculosis Association, trustee of the South Carolina Sanatorium, vice-president of the American Trudeau Society (now the American Thoracic Society), president of the South Carolina Tuberculosis Conference, the Southern Sanatorium Association, and the Southern Tuberculosis Association, as well as the South Carolina Tuberculosis Association. He was a diplomate of the American Board of Internal Medicine.

Dr. Smith was long interested in the Society for the Relief of the Families of Deceased and Disabled Indigent Members of the Medical Profession of the State of South Carolina and served as its president. His interest in this charitable organization led him to propose the establishment of the Benevolence Fund in the South Carolina Medical Association and he was made chairman of the committee which inaugurated it. A bas-relief of Dr. Smith, presented by his medical friends, with appropriate inscription is in the Charleston County Hospital and his portrait is in the Pinehaven area of the Charleston County Hospital. Dr. Smith was for some years regional consultant on tuberculosis to the Veterans' Administration. He was the author of numerous scientific papers and two books, one a story of Pinehaven Sanatorium and the other a biographical account of Leon Banov, M.D.

The inscription on the Pinehaven plaque says "True Physician and Teacher, Humanitarian". These things Dr. Smith was, but there was more to his character. He was a dedicated, vigorous worker in the cause of tuberculosis and was not inclined to accept opposition lying down. He inspired an intense affection and love in his patients. His kind heart and cheerful disposition were characteristic in all his many gregarious activities.

Ill health forced his retirement in 1963, but he never lost his acute interest in his friends and patients, and in the affairs of his profession.

LEONIDAS MICHAEL STOKES
1879-1945

Born near Canadys in Colleton County, Dr. Stokes attended the South Carolina College, where he obtained his A.B. degree in 1902.

For a short time after this he taught school and then entered the Medical Department of the University of Georgia, where he remained for a year before transferring to the Medical College of the State of South Carolina. From the latter he graduated in 1906 and served an internship at Roper Hospital before going to Walterboro to settle. There he entered vigorously into general practice and showed an intense interest in organized medicine.

He was president of the First District Medical Association, of the Colleton County Medical Society, and of the Coastal Medical Society, which last he organized. He was intimately associated with the Esdorn Hospital and served as chairman of his local Board of Health. He was very active in the affairs of the South Carolina Medical Association and was elected to its vice-presidency, succeeding to the presidency upon the resignation of Dr. Julius Taylor in 1937. He also served as a member of the State Board of Medical Examiners and as a trustee of the Medical College.

After some sixteen years of general medicine he pursued postgraduate courses in the diseases of the eye, ear, nose, and throat in New York and confined himself to this specialty. Dr. Stokes was a physician of infinite courtesy and graciousness, a man of keen intellect and wholesome humor. He was highly regarded by all who knew him.

JULIUS HEYWARD TAYLOR
1877-1938

Dr. Taylor was a native of Columbia, the son of Dr. Benjamin W. Taylor. He pursued his education at the South Carolina Military

Academy, where he received his B.S. degree in 1896, thereafter taking two years of pre-medical work at the University of South Carolina. His degree of M.D. was received from the University of Virginia in 1901. After graduation he spent four years in New York City in training at St. Luke's Hospital, Children's Orthopedic Hospital, and the Lying-In Hospital.

Returning to Columbia he engaged in general practice until 1915, when he confined himself to surgery, serving as surgeon to the Southern Railway, the Atlantic Coast Line Railroad, and other companies. He was a pioneer in setting up a small clinic in the slum areas around the Pacific Mills and remained as a medical employee of the mills for his whole life.

During his career he served as president of the Columbia Medical Society, and was a member of the Southern Surgical Association as well as of a number of other medical organizations. He was a fellow of the American College of Surgeons and served on the South Carolina Board of Medical Examiners.

Dr. Taylor was a man with many cultural interests. He was concerned particularly with the history of medicine and contributed papers on that and other subjects. During his latter years he was afflicted with serious heart disease and was constrained to resign the presidency of the South Carolina Medical Association on July 30, 1937. The encomiums at the time of his death said among other things, "Dr. Taylor's uncommon manly beauty was complemented by a courtesy the deeper and more delicate because founded in utmost benevolence and simplicity of spirit. . . . A sweet, a gentle, a clean, high-hearted, gallant gentleman."

LAWRENCE PHILLIPS THACKSTON
1899-1964

A native of Orangeburg County, Dr. Thackston spent practically all of his life there. After completing the local schools and serving  in the infantry during World War I, he went to Clemson College, where he graduated with a B.S. degree in 1920 and earned the reputation of being a fine athlete. Moving on to the Medical College of the State of South Carolina he received his degree of M.D. in 1924 and afterwards pursued postgraduate instruction at Roper Hospital, the Orangeburg Hospital, and the New York Postgraduate Hospital. After achieving his medical degree he was a member of the medical corps in World War II with considerable service in Africa and Europe and advanced to the rank of colonel, achieving two decorations for wounds.

Dr. Thackston was councillor for the Eighth District of the South Carolina Medical Association and was active in supporting the programs of the Association. He had a reputation as a forceful speaker. In 1937 he founded and became director of the Urological Institute, which was later to merge with the Orangeburg Hospital. He was prominent in urological circles and wrote papers on his specialty and also devised a number of urological instruments.

He was president of the Edisto Medical Society and of the Southeastern Section of the American Urological Association, a fellow of the American College of Surgeons, State Regent of the International College of Surgeons, and a diplomate of the American Board of Urology. He also was a member of the honorary fraternity Alpha Omega Alpha. He served the Medical College as a trustee and had many civic and fraternal connections.

Dr. Thackston died in an automobile accident.

WASHINGTON PRICE TIMMERMAN
1869-1938

Son of a physician and a native of Edgefield County, Dr. Timmerman graduated from the Medical College of the State of South Carolina in 1891. He then practiced in Greenwood County and later settled permanently in Batesburg, where he maintained a busy general practice throughout his life.

Dr. Timmerman was president of the Ridge Medical Society, surgeon to the Southern Railway, and vice-president of the Association of Southern Railroad Surgeons. He engaged in many local activities, serving as alderman and as mayor of Batesburg and was active in local politics. He also served as school trustee for a long period. During World War I he served on the Draft Exemption Board with the rank of major in the Medical Reserve Corps. He was largely responsible for the establishment of the Leesville Infirmary.

GEORGE MADISON TRULUCK
1887-1968

Born in Olanta, Dr. Truluck graduated from Clemson College in 1908 and from the Medical College of the State of South Carolina in 1911. He practiced in Marion until World War I, in which he served for two years in Europe as captain in the Army Medical Corps. After his return to this country and a number of courses in his chosen specialty at various medical centers, he came to Orangeburg in 1922 as a specialist in work with the eye, ear, nose, and throat. A fellow of the American College of Surgeons, he later became president of the South Carolina Ophthalmological and Otolaryngological Society.

He served as president of the Edisto Medical Society, and for some years as councillor from the Eighth District to the South Carolina Medical Association before being raised to the presidency. He associated himself with many civic and religious activities.

WILBUR RAYMOND TUTEN
1889-1961

Dr. Tuten, born at Ulmers, attended the Orangeburg Collegiate Institute and the College of Charleston. After his graduation from the Medical College of the State of South Carolina in 1911, he practiced medicine in Fairfax until the time of his death.

Dr. Tuten was always interested in organized medicine, serving as president of the Allendale County Medical Society and of his district society, and as a vice-president of the South Carolina Medical Association before his elevation to the presidency in 1950. He was a member of the State Board of Medical Examiners and on the staff of the Allendale County Hospital.

Dr. Tuten represented the highest class of general practioner. His civic interests were expressed in his position of mayor of Fairfax, which he occupied for eight years. He was also a member of the board of trustees of Fairfax public schools.

WILLIAM ROBERT WALLACE
1882-

Dr. Wallace was born in 1882, took his academic education at Presbyterian College (A.B. 1903), and after a stint of teaching,

graduated from the Medical College of Virginia in Richmond in 1908. He then had experience in the Memorial Hospital in Richmond and the Roper Hospital in Charleston. In 1909 he began his practice in Chester, where he was associated with Dr. Harvey E. McConnell. Together they and others helped organize the Chester Sanatorium and operated the Pryor Hospital for 30 years.

Dr. Wallace is an active practitioner and is highly esteemed in his own locality and elsewhere. In 1922 he became a member of the Executive Committee of the State Board of Health and in 1944 was elected chairman, in which capacity he served until 1967 when he resigned his office, but remained on the committee until 1970. The South Carolina Association of Public Health Physicians presented to Dr. Wallace a testimonial silver bowl at the time of the opening of the new Sims building, headquarters for the State Board of Health. In further recognition, the assembly room in this new building in Columbia was named the W. R. Wallace Room.

His medical connections have been numerous as president of the Chester County Medical Society, president of the Tri-State Medical Association, and a member of the Association of Seaboard Air Line and Railway Surgeons. Dr. Wallace is still in the active practice of medicine.

On the 50th anniversary of his practice, he was honored by his many admirers in Chester by "W. R. Wallace Day".

WILLIAM WESTON, SR.

1874-1962

Born at Eastover of a distinguished South Carolina family and son of a physician, William Weston attended the University of

South Carolina for two years and then graduated from the University of the South Medical School in 1896. He then went on to graduate from the Medical College of the State of South Carolina in 1897. In later years he did work at Harvard, Columbia University and Johns Hopkins University. Recognition of his later accomplishments is attested by the honorary degrees which he received: LL.D. from the University of South Carolina in 1931, doctor of science, University of the South in 1931, doctor of public health, Medical College of the State of South Carolina in 1929, a member of Alpha Omega Alpha, honorary medical fraternity.

After completing his education he went to Columbia and began general practice, which he was to continue until 1908 when he determined to confine himself to pediatrics, probably the second physician in the Southeast to take this step, and studied at Johns Hopkins, Columbia University, and Harvard to this end. Early interest in the problems of hookworm infestation led him to bring about the establishment of a clinic in Columbia for the treatment of this disease. He was interested in teaching and instructed the nurses in Columbia Hospital for many years, and also served as a member of the faculty of the Southern Pediatric Seminar in Saluda for a long period.

Dr. Weston had a turn for organization and promotion and was concerned with many activities in Columbia. He brought about the establishment of the Columbia Children's Clinic and functioned as its head for some time. He organized and was the first chairman of the Section on Pediatrics of the Southern Medical Association, on whose council he also served. He was a founder of the American Academy of Pediatrics and promoted the organization of the Southern Nutritional Association which met at Blowing Rock, N. C. He was chairman of the Pediatric Section of the American Medical Association and for many years delegate from this section to the House of Delegates.

During World War I, Dr. Weston served as major in the Medical Corps and received some training in hospital administration. Returning home, he found the Columbia Hospital in a rather parlous state, and went about with determination to build it into a satisfactory institution. He served as chief of staff and was responsible for reorganization of the services and for obtaining funds for the building of the Nurses Home, which was later named the William Weston Home in his honor. Similarly he worked vigorously with the affairs of the Columbia Medical Society, promoting good will and interest. Specifically, he instigated the publication of *The Recorder* and the organization of outstanding programs which attracted physicians from all over the state.

While he was a busy and respected practitioner, Dr. Weston could find time to devote himself to the intensive study of nutritional diseases. He was particularly concerned with acrodynia, which he was the first to recognize as occurring in this country. He exploited the fact of the high content of iodine in South Carolina foodstuffs, which so intrigued him that as a consequence of his interest he became chairman of the South Carolina Food Research Commission, and promoted investigation of the virtues of iodine and the means of popularizing South Carolina foodstuffs. He devised a vitamin chart which was widely used and reprinted. His many published papers dealt largely with nutritional problems.

Dr. Weston was highly respected, an affable friend, a delightful host. He was honored by the Columbia Medical Society, which he served as president, by a testimonial gift of a silver tray. His portrait by Charles Crowson hangs in the Columbia Hospital. Another portrait commissioned by his many friends is in the Medical University of South Carolina.

WILLIAM WESTON, JR.

1898-

Member of a distinguished medical family and Columbian born and bred, Dr. Weston pursued his preliminary education in local

schools and at the Episcopal High School in Virginia. He entered the University of South Carolina and graduated A.B. before moving on to the University of Virginia where he obtained his degree of M.D. in 1923. After graduation he served an internship at the Johns Hopkins Hospital, was later chief resident of the Children's Hospital in Philadelphia, and was associated with Babies' Hospital and Nursery and Child's Hospital, New York.

He came back to Columbia in 1927 and practiced independently briefly before joining forces with his father, the well recognized pediatrician and an ex-president of the South Carolina Medical Association. Dr. Weston, Jr. has held many responsible offices. He is a fellow of the American Academy of Pediatrics, a diplomate of the American Board of Pediatrics, and formerly chairman of District IV of the American Academy of Pediatrics. He served as chairman of the South Carolina Chapter of the American Academy of Pediatrics, president of the Columbia Medical Society, secretary of the Section on Pediatrics of the Southern Medical Association, and chairman of the Section on Pediatrics of the American Medical Association. For some time he was delegate to the AMA from the South Carolina Medical Association. He has served as consultant to many organizations, written a number of papers, and participated actively in community activities.

THOMAS PRIOLEAU WHALEY
1870-1918

Dr. Whaley, a native of Pendleton but resident of Charleston, received his M.D. degree from the Medical College of the State of

South Carolina in 1892. He served as an intern in the Charleston City Hospital and also in the St. Francis Xavier Infirmary. He did postgraduate work in Vienna and Paris, being interested particularly in surgery, genito-urinary diseases, and dermatology. He also worked with Dr. George Michael Edebohls of New York, who taught him his technique of decapsulation of the kidneys.

Dr. Whaley practiced in Charleston. He acted as the secretary of the South Carolina Medical Association for ten years before his election to the presidency. He was a member of many medical organizations, attended the City Hospital, and was a lecturer to the Training School for Nurses at that institution. He was also a lecturer on dermatology at the Medical College and professor of genito-urinary surgery there for some years.

Dr. Whaley was a very popular physician and was highly esteemed by his patients. He is said to have been one of the first in this area to use spinal anesthesia, one of the first to use the x-ray machine, the first to decapsulate the kidneys, to recognize beri-beri, and to devote much special attention to urology.

CHARLES FREDERICK WILLIAMS
1875-1948

A native of York County, Dr. Williams attended private schools and obtained his degree from the University of Maryland School of Medicine (1899).

He entered practice in York, but in about two years he was commissioned as acting assistant surgeon in the United States Army, serving in 1902 and 1903 in the Philippines. Resigning from the Army in 1903 he took postgraduate work in Baltimore, and in July of that year began general practice in Columbia. There he served as the City Physician in 1904; three years later he became secretary of the State Board of Health, and in 1908 became the state's first state health officer, a position he held for three years, resigning to do postgraduate work in Europe and returning to resume practice in Columbia. In 1911 he organized and conducted the first tuberculosis clinic in Columbia. He served as vice-chairman of the American Medical Association's Section on Preventive Medicine in 1910 and as president of the Columbia Medical Society in 1912.

After preliminary service as a member of the Board of Regents to the South Carolina State Hospital he was appointed superintendent of the hospital May 1, 1915. In this position he was to achieve distinction as an administrator and a true friend of the mentally ill. He made many improvements in the manner of handling the patients, organized a proper medical staff, obtained new buildings and necessary equipment, and removed the political taint from the institution. Dr. Williams maintained great influence in the legislature.

Under his guidance the Negro unit at State Park was developed. He was responsible for establishing the mental hygiene clinics in centrally located cities and towns of the state. He was recognized with the presidential office by a number of organizations: the South

Carolina Hospital Association, the American Psychiatric Association, and the South Carolina Medical Association, and he was a director of the National Committee for Mental Hygiene. He received further recognition of his abilities in the award of the Algernon Sydney Sullivan medal of the University of South Carolina in 1939 and in the following year the honorary degree of doctor of laws. He was a diplomate of the American Board of Psychiatry and Neurology. For many years he served as professor of psychiatry at the Medical College.

In 1920 the name of his institution was changed from The State Hospital for the Insane to The South Carolina State Hospital. There was constant effort to secure more funds. In 1937, at the request of the employees, the new admission building at the Columbia unit was named the Williams Building.

After thirty years of outstanding service, Dr. Williams retired, receiving many tributes from patients and colleagues alike, one of them a plaque for distinguished services (1934) from the South Carolina American Legion. The Columbia Medical Society presented him with a silver pitcher and tray upon his retirement and the hospital personnel had his portrait painted by Charles Crowson. It hangs now in the administration building of the State Hospital. He continued to hold the position of director of research, in which capacity he accomplished much in promoting support for substantial projects at the hospital. Dr. Williams had a commanding appearance, the manners of a true southern gentleman, with a genial personality, which combined courtesy, compassion, and gentleness with a deep religious faith.

ROBERT WILSON
1867-1946

Born in Stateburg, S. C. August 23, 1867, Dr. Robert Wilson came of a line of physicians extending back to the early colonial

days in South Carolina. He was a large figure in the history of medicine in this state and his reputation extended widely over the South and into other parts of the country. He was a person who commanded respect and whose bearing was always one of dignity. An eminent medical educator, he added to his accomplishments a deep interest in cultural and historical matters.

He graduated from the South Carolina College (A.B.) in 1887 and from the Medical College of the State of South Carolina in 1892. After this he pursued instruction at the New York Postgraduate Medical School and continued to keep abreast of the rapidly moving medical world throughout his life. Soon after graduation from the Medical College he taught at his alma mater and rose to the position of professor of medicine and nervous diseases in 1905. Later he became head of the department of medicine. In 1908 he became dean and served in this capacity 35 years, at the end of which time he received the title of dean emeritus.

Dr. Wilson's keen mind led him early to pursue activities in many medical organizations. He was a vigorous participant at many meetings and conventions. He became president of the Medical Society of South Carolina, president of the Tri-State Medical Association, of the Southern Medical Association, and of the South Carolina Medical Association, and was a first vice-president of the American Medical Association (1909-1910). He was physician-in-chief of Roper Hospital and served for many years as chairman of the Executive Committee of the South Carolina State Board of Health. Three honorary degrees were awarded to him, LL.D. by the University of South Carolina, the same degree by the College of Charleston, and the degree of D.C.L. by the University of the South.

Dr. Wilson was one of the early editors of the *Journal of the South Carolina Medical Association* and was the organizer and moving spirit of the Medical History Club of Charleston, whose name was later changed to the Robert Wilson Medical History Club of Charleston. He received numerous honors. The American Legion plaque was conferred on him in 1938 for meritorious services. His portrait was commissioned by a group of admiring physician friends and now hangs in the Roper Hospital. Another likeness is in the Medical University.

Dr. Wilson was the author of many articles on a variety of subjects, including tuberculosis, heart disease, educational preparation, and historical matters. He was a member of Sigma Alpha Epsilon and Phi Chi fraternities, a member of the American Society of Tropical Medicine, the American Clinical and Climatological Association (once its vice-president), a fellow of the American College of Physicians, and many other professional organizations.

Dr. Wilson served as city bacteriologist shortly after graduation and was interested in matters of public health throughout his life. "The Dean" was a large figure in South Carolina, known to the entire profession, and respected for his ability and accomplishments in education and scientific matters. He finally became professor emeritus of medicine. His last position at the Medical College was that of special lecturer on medical history.

ROBERT WILSON, JR.

1905-

Dr. Robert Wilson, Jr., descendant of a long line of South Carolina physicians and the son of Dr. Robert Wilson, who was for

many years the dean and moving spirit in the Medical College of the State of South Carolina, was born in Charleston on May 3, 1905, received the A.B. degree at Princeton University, and was graduated in medicine at the Medical College of the State of South Carolina in 1930. He served hospital appointments at the University Hospital, Baltimore, and at the Boston City Hospital and began the practice of internal medicine in Charleston in 1933. He is a member of Phi Beta Kappa and Alpha Omega Alpha.

Dr. Wilson has been a member of the faculty of the Medical College since that time and is now clinical professor of medicine. He has been certified by the American Board of Internal Medicine (1942) and has been a fellow of the American College of Physicians since 1938. He served a nine-year term in the board of governors of the last named body, and followed this service by a term as regent.

Dr. Wilson acted in many official capacities in medical organizations, having been secretary and later president of the Medical Society of South Carolina (Charleston) for two terms of two years each. He promoted ably the affairs of Roper Hospital in its expansion program. He was elected secretary of the South Carolina Medical Association in 1953, its president in 1963, and has always maintained a very active interest in the affairs of organized medicine. He served as a director of the South Carolina Hospital Service Plan for many years.

He has had many hobbies and a fancy for local politics, as indicated by his service on Charleston City Council. Once a president of the Poetry Society, a vestryman of St. Michael's Church, vice-president of the St. Andrew's Society, a member of the South Carolina Society, the St. Cecilia Society, the Carolina Yacht Club, and the Kiwanis Club, his many connections attest to the multiplicity of his interests and to his ability.

CHARLES NEWTON WYATT
1904-

Charles N. Wyatt was born in Easley, S. C. January 3, 1904, the son of Charles Newton and Addis Pickens Wyatt. His father and

an uncle practiced medicine in Easley for a number of years.

Dr. Wyatt was educated in the public schools of Easley, attended Wofford College for one year and the College of Charleston for two years. He graduated from the Medical College of the State of South Carolina in 1927, and trained at St. Francis Xavier Infirmary in Charleston and Emma Moss Booth Memorial Hospital in Greenville. He started practicing medicine in Laurens in November 1928 and later returned to Greenville in the office of Dr. Hugh Smith.

Dr. Wyatt served nearly five years in the Army of the United States in World War II. Entering as a captain of the Medical Corps in June 1941, he advanced to the rank of colonel in August 1944. He was chief of the Medical Service Station, Camp Forrest, Tenn., and commanded field hospitals in Iran and station hospitals in Iran, Italy, and Okinawa. Honorably discharged from service in February 1946, he resumed general practice in Greenville early in that year and has continued actively until the present.

He has served as president of the Greenville County Medical Society, president of the South Carolina Chapter of the American Academy of General Practice, delegate to the AAGP for many years, working on several committees, alternate delegate to the American Medical Association, serving as delegate at the interim session in Minneapolis, December 1958. A member of the Council of the South Carolina Medical Association for nine years, he sat as chairman in 1959-1960, as chairman of the Committee of Civil Defense of the SCMA for five years and as a member of the Committee on Disaster Medical Care of the Council on National Security of the American Medical Association.

He has been a member of the Lions Club of Greenville for 35 years and was its president in 1948-1949. He is a member of the Country Club of Greenville, a 32nd Degree Mason and a member of the Ancient Arabic Order of the Mystic Shrine. He is medical director of Hejaz Temple of Shrine, a member of the Trinity Lutheran Church, Greenville, and a member of the Chamber of Commerce of Greenville and that of the United States.

Since 1956 he has practiced general medicine in partnership with Dr. Horace M. Whitworth.

The Greenville County Medical Society presented Dr. Wyatt in 1961 a handsomely engraved silver tray for his tireless efforts on the part of organized medicine. Recently, Dr. Wyatt was honored in surprise ceremonies by his patients and friends with a portrait of himself to be hung in the new St. Francis Community Hospital. The hospital doctors dining room and the cardiac receiving room will bear his name.

JOEL WENTWORTH WYMAN
1911-

Dr. Wyman was born in Estill, S. C. and graduated from the University of South Carolina and the Medical College of the State of South Carolina. He comes of a family associated for six generations with South Carolina medicine.

He served his internship at McLeod Infirmary in Florence and then practiced medicine in Anderson from 1946-1949. In 1949 he became assistant resident at Boston City Hospital, where he studied dermatology. In the following year he was a clinical fellow at Massachusetts General Hospital and in 1951 a fellow at Duke University Hospital.

A staff member of Anderson Memorial Hospital, Dr. Wyman has been practicing dermatology in Anderson since 1952. He was certified by the American Board of Dermatology in 1953.

Dr. Wyman is a member of the Anderson County Medical Society, the American Medical Association, a fellow of the American Academy of Dermatology, and a member of the Southern Medical Association.

He is a past president of the Anderson County Medical Society, was state chairman of SCALPEL for two years, state chairman of AMA-ERF for two years, and has also served on numerous committees of the South Carolina Medical Association.

JAMES ROGERS YOUNG
1882-1969

Dr. Young was born in Due West and grew up to attend Erskine College, from which he received the degree of A.B. in 1901. He then proceeded to Vanderbilt University where he achieved his medical degree in 1906. After some postgraduate work abroad, he went to Anderson, becoming in time president of the county and district medical societies and an active worker in many civic and religious affairs. He was a member of City Council, the school board, the Chamber of Commerce, and other organizations.

Dr. Young pursued a surgical practice. He was one of the founders of the Rose Ramer Cancer Clinic at the Anderson Hospital, and gave much of his time to its activities. He also provided an auditorium for the hospital. In 1922 he became a fellow of the American College of Surgeons. An honorary degree of LL.D. was conferred upon him by Erskine College in 1943 and he was long a member of the board of trustees of this institution. He was among the organizers of the Southeastern Surgical Congress and the Piedmont Postgraduate Clinical Assembly, serving as president of the former in 1953. He also served as president of the executive committee of the South Carolina Division of the American Cancer Society.

OTHER BIOGRAPHIES

While the list of presidents of South Carolina Medical Association includes the majority of the physicians of the state who were most active and productive in organized medicine, there were many other members of the Association whose contributions were large. To judge the relative merits of these physicians is practically impossible. At the real risk of having his selection seriously questioned, the author has added a few biographical sketches of several persons, who, in his opinion, contributed greatly to our medical affairs of the 20th century.

JAMES WOODS BABCOCK
1856-1922

Because of his activity at what is now the South Carolina State Hospital, and his important work in recognition and control of

pellagra, Dr. Babcock's name was very familiar not only to South Carolinians of his generation but to many others of the medical world.

Born in Chester, a son of Dr. Sidney E. Babcock, who was a surgeon in the Confederate Army, he was educated at Phillips Academy (Exeter) and Harvard College, receiving his degree of bachelor of arts in 1882 and graduating four years later from the Harvard Medical School. He spent five years at the McLean Asylum, in Somerville (later Waverly, Mass.), before accepting the superintendency of the State Lunatic Asylum in Columbia, a position to which

he devoted many years of dedicated service until he resigned in 1914.

He was responsible for making many beneficial administrative, physical, and therapeutic changes at the hospital, including establishment of a school of nursing, and was active in the investigation of many important problems in psychiatry and in tuberculosis in mental patients. He served as professor of mental diseases at the Medical College of the State of South Carolina from 1915 until his death. His influence in the General Assembly produced many constructive pieces of legislation related to mental health.

In 1914, petty jealousies and small politics in the General Assembly led to an investigation of the State Hospital which eventually resulted in complete exoneration of Dr. Babcock's administration. The unpleasantness of this process impelled him to resign from his position. After leaving the employ of the state in 1914, he organized Waverley Sanitarium in Columbia, a private hospital for psychiatric patients, and continued to direct this institution until his death in 1922.

Observations of patients with pellagra in the hospital led Dr. Babcock to intensive study of the disease there and in Italy. He observed these local patients in 1907 and is credited with being the first to emphasize the prevalence of pellagra in this country and to work toward a solution of that problem. With Dr. C. H. Lavinder he translated A. Marie's *La Pellagre*, which had served to establish the disease as a clinical entity. His writings about the disease appeared in national journals. He was largely responsible for the organization of a international conference on pellagra sponsored by his Board of Regents and held in Columbia in October 1908, and again in 1909 and 1910.

Dr. Babcock was a man of culture, a lover of literature and old books, and a collector of antique furniture. He contributed much to beautifying the grounds of the State Hospital. He served on the Columbia Water and Sewer Commissions and Board of Health, was one time a member of the South Carolina Legislature and a member of the Executive Committee of the State Board of Health. He received an honorary degree (LL.D.) from the University of South Carolina in 1905, and founded the National Association for the Study of Pellagra, of which he was president for three years. A building at the State Hospital bears his name.

REFERENCES

Dictionary of American Biography, Ed. by Allen Johnson. (New York: Charles Scribner's Sons, 1964), p. 458. Henry R. Viets, M.D., author.

William S. Hall, M.D., "Psychiatrist, Humanitarian, and Scholar, James Woods Babcock, M.D.", *J. S. Carolina Med. Ass.,* 66:366 (October 1970).

EDGAR ALPHONSO HINES
1867-1940

Dr. Hines for many years was the soul and the chief executive of organized medicine in South Carolina.

Serving as secretary, editor, treasurer, and general promoter of the South Carolina Medical Association, he was the backbone of that organization and carried it through many difficult times.

Dr. Hines was born in Wayne County, N. C. His father, a North Carolinian, was a Confederate veteran who pursued a career of railroad construction which carried him to a number of different areas. In 1886 the family moved to Brunson, S. C. Here Edgar Hines decided to give up his original thought of studying engineering and turned to medicine as a career. He received a classical education at the Bingham School in North Carolina. Funds were not readily available to continue his education, and he worked at many things to secure the wherewithal for his education, now on the farm or in the machine shop or building bridges or serving in stores. These rather arduous activities possibly contributed to the remarkable health which persisted throughout his life. During his years at the Medical College of the State of South Carolina he also worked at many jobs before obtaining his medical degree in 1891, after taking an optional third year of instruction.

After graduation he settled briefly in Gillisonville, Hampton County, where he organized the local physicians into a society and was promptly elected president. He then went to the hamlet of Calhoun and pursued some studies in chemistry at nearby Clemson College. His next move was to Seneca, where he interested himself in a number of local civic activities, and among other things, initiated school medical inspection.

His thirst for knowledge was not satisfied and in 1898 he studied at Johns Hopkins Hospital and throughout his life attended numerous postgraduate courses, both in this country and abroad. He became superintendent of the Anderson Hospital, and during his one year of service visited many sections of the state and encouraged the building of other county hospitals. He was one of the founders of the South Carolina Hospital Association and was particularly active in obtaining a hospital for his home county of Oconee.

In the first World War Dr. Hines served on the draft board briefly, was a medical member of the District Exemption Board, and assisted with the voluntary medical corps. After the war began he applied for a commission and was given the title of major and served at Emergency Hospital Number 52. At the age of 64 he was transferred from the active service to the auxiliary reserve.

Early in his career Dr. Hines began to write medical papers and to participate in the business of organized medicine. He became a delegate to the state medical association and served on many committees. He was secretary and president of the Fourth District Society and became secretary of the South Carolina Medical Association in 1910, and in 1911 was made editor-in-chief of its *Journal* after serving three years as associate editor. In 1912 the offices of secretary and treasurer were merged and he assumed both positions. In 1909 he first became a delegate to the AMA and gave many years of service thereafter.

While Dr. Hines was a general practitioner, he had intense interest in preventive medicine and in pediatrics. In 1909 he became a member of the Executive Committee of the State Board of Health and served for a long term. He was one of the organizers of the South Carolina Public Health Association and the founder of the Bureau of Child Hygiene. In 1913, he served as section chairman of the International Congress of School Hygiene and later as chairman of the section on public health in the Southern Medical Association.

His pediatric interest was developed early and continued to be very active. He was a charter member of the faculty of the Southern Pediatric Seminar at Saluda and on his 68th birthday he passed the examination of the American Board of Pediatrics. He was one of the organizers of the South Carolina Pediatric Society, its first secretary and subsequently its president, and also was active in the American Public Health Association.

Dr. Hines in 1914 was president of the Alumni Association of the Medical College and was the first president of the Piedmont Postgraduate Clinical Assembly in Anderson.

He was a member of many scientific organizations and showed great interest in the history of medicine. He was twice chairman of the Conference of State Secretaries and Editors of State Medical Journals and a charter member of the Interstate Postgraduate Association. His contributions to South Carolina were many.

BENJAMIN OTIS WHITTEN
1886-1970

Born in Pendleton, S. C. in 1886, Dr. Whitten obtained a common school education and attended Emory University, from whose

medical school he graduated with honors in 1913. During his school days he supported himself by working as a telegraph operator.

After graduation he returned to South Carolina and did rural practice for three years before going to the State Hospital in Columbia for training in psychiatry. He spent three years there, and when the proposed State Training School for the Feeble-Minded was created by the legislature, he was selected to take charge of the institution, which opened in 1920 with six pupils. Under the careful and dedicated guidance of Dr. Whitten, the institution now has over 2,500 children and utilizes 50 buildings. In 1954 the name of the Training School was changed to Whitten Village in honor of Dr. Whitten. From 1934 Dr. Whitten also conducted the Girls Industrial School.

During the first World War Dr. Whitten volunteered for service but was directed to remain in charge of the school. In 1931-1932 he spent about two years organizing a similar institution in Utah.

He was president of the American Association on Mental Deficiency and has occupied a most respected place in the field of this interest.

Dr. Whitten performed a remarkable job in developing Whitten Village. He had to contend with the vagaries of the legislature over the years and had to put up with political and other pressures for favoritism in admissions to the school. He handled the situation well and showed himself a man of extraordinary ability and vision.

He retired in 1965 after 47 years of service. He died in November 1970.

APPENDIX

STATE BOARD OF MEDICAL EXAMINERS

After several changes in composition and prerogatives since its inception in 1817, the Licensing Board was reconstituted in 1894, when it became composed of seven men appointed by the governor to hold sole authority in matters of licensure. In 1897 the members were elected by the South Carolina Medical Association and recommended to the governor for appointment. Later an eighth member was added.

On February 19, 1900 a seven-man board of medical examiners was again established, one member from each congressional district by appointment of the governor. Later, in 1904, the "member-at-large" was nominated by the South Carolina Medical Association. By a legislative act of 1901, graduates of the Medical College of the State of South Carolina were exempted from the customary examination, but this privilege was rescinded in the following year.

Requirements were stiffened on July 1, 1914, when it was stipulated that the applicant must have a diploma from a reputable medical college of four full years consecutive courses. Three years later a diploma from a reputable medical college of at least Class B standing was required and in 1920 diplomas from only Class A medical schools were acceptable. Under the present provisions of the board, at least three years of pre-medical work and a diploma from a Class A school are required. The board is appointed by the governor on the recommendations of the South Carolina Medical Association and meets twice a year for its examinations. The act of 1920 is the version now in use.

At present one year of postgraduate training is required for licensing. South Carolina endorses licentiates of all states and diplomates of the National Board. Endorsement is on an individual basis, with the right reserved to reconsider an applicant when uncomplimentary data is received during investigation and processing of applications. Florida and one or two other states do not endorse licentiates of the South Carolina Board.

A LIST OF PRESIDENTS OF THE SOUTH CAROLINA MEDICAL ASSOCIATION SINCE 1900

Meeting Place	Date	President	Address
Charleston	1900	W. P. Porcher	Charleston
Florence	1901	G. R. Dean	Spartanburg
Spartanburg	1902	T. G. Croft	Aiken
Sumter	1903	Manning Simons	Charleston
Darlington	1904	E. F. Darby	Magnolia
Greenville	1905	Robert Wilson	Charleston
Columbia	1906	Davis Furman	Greenville
Bennettsville	1907	T. P. Whaley	Charleston
Anderson	1908	LeGrand Guerry	Columbia
Summerville	1909	S. C. Baker	Sumter
Laurens	1910	J. L. Dawson	Charleston
Charleston	1911	J. H. McIntosh	Columbia
Columbia	1912	J. W. Jervey	Greenville
Rock Hill	1913	C. M. Rees	Charleston
Florence	1914	William Weston	Columbia
Greenwood	1915	E. F. Parker	Charleston
Charleston	1916	G. A. Neuffer	Abbeville
Spartanburg	1917	C. B. Earle	Greenville
Aiken	1918	F. H. McLeod	Florence
Florence	1919	J. A. Hayne	Columbia
Greenville	1920	E. W. Pressly	Greenville
Columbia	1921	W. P. Timmerman	Batesburg
Rock Hill	1922	H. L. Shaw	Sumter
Charleston	1923	C. F. Williams	Columbia
Orangeburg	1924	L. O. Mauldin	Greenville
Spartanburg	1925	D. M. Crosson	Leesville
Sumter	1926	R. S. Cathcart	Charleston
Anderson	1927	G. H. Bunch	Columbia
Columbia	1928	D. L. Smith	Spartanburg
Charleston	1929	R. E. Hughes	Laurens
Florence	1930	C. R. May	Bennettsville
Greenville	1931	K. M. Lynch	Charleston
Columbia	1932	C. A. Mobley	Orangeburg
Spartanburg	1933	J. R. Young	Anderson
Charleston	1934	R. E. Abell	Chester
Florence	1935	Wm. Egleston (died in office)	Hartsville
		S. E. Harmon	Columbia
Greenville	1936	S. E. Harmon (died in office)	Columbia
		R. C. Bruce	Greenville
Columbia	1937	R. C. Bruce	Greenville
Myrtle Beach	1938	J. H. Taylor (resigned)	Columbia
		L. M. Stokes	Walterboro
Spartanburg	1939	J. H. DesPortes	Fort Mill
Charleston	1940	Douglas Jennings	Bennettsville
Greenville	1941	W. L. Pressly	Due West

Meeting Place	Date	President	Address
Columbia	1942	G. M. Truluck	Orangeburg
Columbia	1943	T. A. Pitts	Columbia
Columbia	1944	W. A. Smith	Charleston
Columbia	1945	W. R. Wallace	Chester
Myrtle Beach	1946	W. T. Brockman	Greenville
Myrtle Beach	1947	J. C. McLeod	Florence
Charleston	1948	O. B. Chamberlain	Charleston
Myrtle Beach	1949	R. B. Durham	Columbia
Myrtle Beach	1950	Roderick Macdonald	Rock Hill
Myrtle Beach	1951	W. R. Tuten	Fairfax
Myrtle Beach	1952	J. D. Guess	Greenville
Columbia	1953	L. P. Thackston	Orangeburg
Myrtle Beach	1954	C. R. F. Baker	Sumter
Charleston	1955	T. R. Gaines	Anderson
Myrtle Beach	1956	O. B. Mayer	Columbia
Myrtle Beach	1957	W. H. Prioleau	Charleston
Myrtle Beach	1958	D. L. Smith, Jr.	Spartanburg
Columbia	1959	R. L. Crawford	Lancaster
Myrtle Beach	1960	Wm. Weston, Jr.	Columbia
Charleston	1961	J. P. Cain, Jr.	Mullins
Myrtle Beach	1962	C. N. Wyatt	Greenville
Myrtle Beach	1963	J. H. Gressette	Orangeburg
Myrtle Beach	1964	Robert Wilson	Charleston
Myrtle Beach	1965	F. C. Owens	Columbia
Myrtle Beach	1966	J. P. Price	Florence
Myrtle Beach	1967	G. D. Johnson	Spartanburg
Myrtle Beach	1968	N. O. Eaddy	Sumter
Myrtle Beach	1969	J. W. Wyman	Anderson
Myrtle Beach	1970	W. L. Perry	Chesterfield
Myrtle Beach	1971	Ben N. Miller	Columbia

A LIST OF SECRETARIES OF THE SOUTH CAROLINA MEDICAL ASSOCIATION

1900	T. P. Whaley, Rec. Sec.
	A. J. Buist, Cor. Sec.
1901	T. P. Whaley, Rec. Sec.
	W. Weston, Cor. Sec.
1902-1903	T. P. Whaley, Rec. Sec.
	A. B. Knowlton, Cor. Sec.
1904-1905	T. P. Whaley, Secretary
1906-1909	Walter Cheyne, Secretary
1910-1940	Edgar A. Hines, Secretary
	(Secretary & Treasurer, 1912-1940)
1941-1950	Julian P. Price, Secretary-Treasurer
1951-1952	N. B. Heyward, Secretary
1953-1962	Robert Wilson, Secretary
1963-1968	Ben N. Miller, Secretary
1969-1971	D. Strother Pope, Secretary

INDEX

A

Abbeville County Medical Society, 41
Abell, Dr. R. E., biog. 97, 188
Aesculapian (The), 87
Aiken County Medical Society, 42
Aimar, Dr. C. P., 8, 45, 95
Allendale County Medical Society, 42
Alms House, Charleston, 72
Alumni Bulletin of the Medical University of South Carolina, 92
American Academy of General Practice, South Carolina Chapter, 71, 91
American Academy of Pediatrics, South Carolina Chapter, 71
American College of Surgeons, South Carolina Chapter, 70
American Medical Association, 7, 95, 174
American Psychiatric Association, South Carolina District Branch, 71-72, 73
American Public Health Association, 36, 39
Anderson County Medical Society, 42
Anderson County Memorial Hospital, 42, 94
Anti-Tuberculosis Committee, 11
Aycock, Dr. Kenneth, 31, 37

B

Babcock Center, 74
Babcock, Dr. J. W., 72, 74, biog. 181
Babcock, Dr. Sidney E., 181
Baker, Dr. A. E., 95
Baker, Dr. C. R. F., 99
Baker, Dr. C. R. F. (Sumter), biog. 98, 189
Baker, Dr. S. C., 61, 98, biog. 99, 154, 188
Baker-Dick Infirmary, 99
Baker Sanatorium Bulletin, 87
Ball, Dr. Austin, 95
Bamberg County Medical Society, 42
Bamberg, Mrs. Joan, 92
Banov, Dr. Leon, 36, 37
Barbot, Dr. L. D., 44
Barker, Miss Ruth, 92
Barnwell County Medical Society, 43
Barth, Dr. Ira, 91
Bates, Dr. L. B., 44
Bates, Dr. Phillips, 69
Bauer, Dr. Vernon L., 61
Baxter, Dr. D., 77
Beaufort County Medical Society, 43
Beaufort-Jasper Medical Society, 43, 55
Beckman, Dr. William P., 73

Bell, Dr. F. A., 52
Bennettsville Hospital, 126
Bennettsville Medical Meeting (annual), 126
Berkeley County Medical Society, 43
Black, Dr. W. A., 66, 67
Blackman, Dr. Lyndell W., 78
Blue Cross, 15, 19
Blue Shield, 19, 20, 103, 122
Boone, Dr. John, 26
Bossard, Dr. J. J., 99
Boyd, Dr. William, 37
Boykin, Dr. E. M., 56
Brabham, Dr. James, 39
Brabham, Dr. V. W., 51
Bristow, Dr. W. J., 89
Brockman, Dr. W. T., 53, 90, biog. 100, 189
Brown, Dr. Carroll, 66
Browning, Dr. A. W., 51
Bruce, Dr. R. C., biog. 101, 188
Brunson, Dr. Sophia, 64
Buist, Dr. A. J., 95, 189
Buist, Dr. J. Somers, 24
Bulletin of the Anderson County Hospital, 15, 88, 91
Bulletin of the Greenville County Medical Society, 53, 88, 90
Bulletin of the Pee Dee Medical Association, 67, 88, 91, 103
Bulletin of the Woman's Auxiliary, South Carolina Medical Association, 19
Bullock, Dr. J. R., 57
Bunch, Dr. George H., 79, biog. 102, 188
Burdell, Dr. W. J., 56
Burnett, Dr. A. W., 56
Burroughs, Dr. H. H., 55
Busch, Dr. John F., 80
Byrnes, Gov. James F., 73

C

Cain, Dr. Joseph P., 67, 88, 91, biog. 103, 189
Calhoun County Medical Society, 43, 51
Camden Medical Society, 56
Cantey, Dr. William C., 71, 79
Carolina Industrial Medical Association, 69
Carolina Sanitarium, 124
Carolina Urological Association, 69
Cathcart, Dr. R. S., 12, 95, biog. 104, 188
Caughman, Gresham, 37
Chamberlain, Dr. Olin B., 75, biog. 105, 189